Inscribed for

Mrs. Toivo Johnson
by her friend,
Archibald Rutledge

November 29, 1960

# THE WORLD
# AROUND HAMPTON

# THE WORLD
# AROUND HAMPTON

*by*

ARCHIBALD RUTLEDGE

*Photographs by* JAY SHULER

THE **BOBBS-MERRILL** COMPANY, INC.
A SUBSIDIARY OF HOWARD W. SAMS & CO., INC.
*Publishers* • INDIANAPOLIS • NEW YORK

*Dedicated to*
*Garland Wingfield Cook*
*and*
*Jean Lindsay Cook,*

two precious little girls
who merit and who have
all my love and all my
admiration.

# Contents

The Yearly Pageant . . . . . . . . 13

## Spring

A Satanic Jaunt . . . . . . . . . . 29

The Lilies
of Tarleton's Deep . . . . . . . . 55

## Summer

Drama in Two Acts . . . . . . . . 73

Plantation Dwellers . . . . . . . . 91

## Autumn

A Nice Arrangement . . . . . . . . 109

The Kings of Curlew Island . . . . . . 131

## Winter

The Swamp in Spate . . . . . . . . 159

My Winter Woods . . . . . . . . 179

# Illustrations

PAGE

Hampton Plantation . . . . . . . . . . 16
The River, Looking Toward the Delta . . . . 23
Old St. James Parish Church . . . . . . . . 23
Will, a Fine Hunter . . . . . . . . . . 34
A Hunter's Boat in the Rice Fields . . . . . . 49
The Rosebud Orchid, *Cleistes divaricata* . . . . 58
The Marshes . . . . . . . . . . . . 64
The Sinister Pitcher Plants . . . . . . . . 68
The "First Flower of the Country," the Camellia . 81
Refuge for the Hunted, an Island in the Delta . . 86
Oak by the River . . . . . . . . . . . 94
The Great House . . . . . . . . . . . 96
Under the Front Porch of Hampton . . . . . 99
A Quiet Cypress Pool . . . . . . . . . 116
Lock and Key on the Ballroom Door . . . . . 127
Hunting Horn on Horn of the Hunted . . . . 133
Doe, Feeding . . . . . . . . . . . . 139

|                                                                              | PAGE |
| ---------------------------------------------------------------------------- | ---- |
| Some White Ibis . . . . . . . . . . . .                                      | 145  |
| A Lagoon . . . . . . . . . . . .                                             | 145  |
| A Whippoorwill . . . . . . . . . . .                                         | 168  |
| The Cardinal, Bird of Beauty, Known from New York to Venezuela . . . . . . . . . | 168  |
| An Egret . . . . . . . . . . . .                                             | 172  |
| The Mantel and Fireplace in the Ballroom . . .                              | 181  |
| The Screech Owl . . . . . . . . . .                                          | 190  |

# THE WORLD
# AROUND HAMPTON

# The Yearly Pageant

HAMPTON PLANTATION is in the wilderness, fifty miles north of Charleston, South Carolina. The property has been in my family since 1686 and is now recorded in my name, but I am not foolish enough to think of this plantation as exclusively mine. There are many to question my undisputed ownership of the land, what is on it and under it: the Negroes who work the land, the wild animals that make it their home, the silent ancestors buried in the ancient churchyard—all have a claim to the place.

About a hundred Negroes, the descendants of slaves, live on the plantation with me. In their minds it is not my place; it is ours. This communal ownership is often brought home to me. But Steve, my woodcutter, has perhaps put it most succinctly.

Late one winter afternoon I walked out into the woods where he had been working all day and I complimented him on the magnificent pile of oak and hickory he had cut. On visiting the place early the next morning, however, I found but a few scattered sticks left. Old Steve had been cutting for me by day and hauling for himself by night. When I approached him about it, I ended my somewhat heated oration by saying, "Steve, I just don't see how you and I can live on the same place any longer."

He eyed me with surprise and mild curiosity. Then he really set me back on my heels.

"Cap'n," he asked, "where is you goin'?"

In spring, that intermission between the barrenness of winter and the bounty of summer, I turn my efforts to the planting of trees and shrubs in the gardens of Hampton. In this case the wildwood is brought to the plantation, for the garden is composed of wild azalea, dogwood, holly, sweet bay, sundew and many other natives of the woods, each carefully transplanted. They surround the house with the joy of the woodlands. I accomplish this task with the help of the colored girls who, supposedly, work under my supervision. But at times my zealous helpers unanimously veto my directions, and then it is as though I had never spoken.

One spring day I found in bloom a wild crab apple on the edge of a thick swamp. The tree was far too large to be moved, but, hunting near it, I found about a dozen seedlings. They are deceptive little bushes, for some are only shoots from large roots and cannot be transplanted. At last I found one I thought had come up from a seed. A little digging convinced me that it had a fine ball of fibrous roots. I returned home for some tools and spent the rest of the morning transplanting the insignificant little sprig in my yard.

This particular flowering crab, now almost as large as one ever grows, is a delight to everyone who visits the plantation. In the woodlands, because of the crowding of other trees, my crab apple would have grown tall and rather scraggly; but on an open lawn it steadily flourished and became a large, symmetrical shrub laden with applelike blossoms.

So great was my delight that day in the feel and the fragrance of the good earth that another

Hampton Plantation

thought assailed me: I would grow trees in pots and cans. First, in the huge cool room under the ballroom I lined up some one hundred fifty flowerpots and cans filled with a mixture of sand and leaf mold sifted—soil I knew the young trees would like. Then, under the eaves above this room I placed big metal containers to catch the rain water, so that watering the little plants would be an easier task.

Having made these preparations I set off into the woods with a trowel and a basket filled with damp sphagnum moss. Choosing damp places, I could easily pull up little cedars, maples, pines, cypresses, sparkleberries and a score of others. It is amazing how many tiny trees, infants of the great forest, one can find in a wildwood.

Burying the transplants in the wet sphagnum moss of my basket, I carried them home, planted them in my prepared pots and cans and watered them. Three or four such trips into the wilds sufficed to fill all my containers.

I left the little trees in the cool cellar for nearly a week, sprinkling them every day. It was a rewarding task, for in all the world there are no odors so natural and wholesome as those of the earth and of the freshness of growing things. After they had become firmly set in their containers, I called for my helpers—Julia and Rosie, Tina, Maple and the others. I wanted them to open a long trench in the shade of the garden, as deep as the tallest pot or can, where I could bury the containers to keep them cool. I pointed out the place I had chosen.

As I have said, my helpers never hesitate to revoke one of my decisions. After picking a spot that suited them, and digging a trench to their satisfaction, my good girls carried there all my little potted trees and packed them sturdily in the ground. They were straight and green and appeared totally disinclined to wilt. An early heavy rain settled them perfectly, and they grew. In view of this success, how could I possibly complain?

The wild life around Hampton, so profuse and vigorously dedicated to sustaining itself, is a constant reminder of another claim to the land. One spring my bedroom window, which overlooks the plantation garden, framed the gentle adventure of two cardinals nesting. Unimpressed by my presence in the house, they chose a spirea bush within three feet of the window. And from the time they began the frail foundation of their home until the young had flown, I had an unusual opportunity to watch them establish squatter's rights.

Both birds helped construct the nest, though the female was the chief designer and builder. Toward the end the mother did everything, just as a human mother is the one who puts the finishing touches on a home. While the eggs were being laid the birds were always together, usually by my pool or in the nearby bushes, talking in excited joy or singing their clear liquid notes. As soon as the female began to set, the male visited her every half hour or so to bring her food. She delicately accepted it from him without changing her position on the nest.

Between these visits he sang almost incessantly, as if to reassure her that he was near. And to my surprise the female also sang as she brooded her eggs. To me the notes of the male and the female sounded identical. When they did not sing outright to each other, they called softly.

Sometimes the male would come to the nest just for a little visit. At such times, and sometimes when she was alone, the mother would leave the eggs and, perched on the rim of the nest, would inspect them carefully. With her bill she would adjust the lining of the nest and pick off ants, and so attend to her business of cleaning house. The master of the house tried to help with this work but, like many men at such times, was far more bother than assistance.

When the little ones were hatched, both birds fed them continually. Yet the babies never seemed to get enough.

They remained in the nest twelve days. When the time came for them to try their wings, the male took up a position in a small apricot tree about fifteen feet away—his scarlet coat the goal toward which they would fly. The mother fluttered toward him and alighted, to show the youngsters what to do.

Three of the four made the first flight successfully, calling all the while. The fourth landed on the ground, whereupon both mother and father flew down to him, chattered to him and coaxed him until he, too, flapped wildly up into the apricot tree.

The next great adventure was a flight to a thick rosebush twenty feet away. They accomplished this feat late the same day. At twilight I went to the bush to see how they would pass the night. There on a sheltered branch of the rosebush was the mother, with two babies on either side of her. Nearby was the proud father.

*The Yearly Pageant*

Who can say they do not own a piece of Hampton?

Though I readily admit the just claims of birds, I do have to exercise some selection in filtering out objectionable settlers. One summer morning at five o'clock our plantation world was silent save for the calling of quail, cardinals, orchard orioles and a wood thrush. I strolled down toward my twenty-acre camellia and azalea garden. Hearing a little sound, I was cautious in case it should mean the presence of a deer or a wild turkey.

Immediately to the north of the garden is the river, and beyond that lies almost boundless wild delta country. On the brink of the dusky bluff above the river, I detected a movement; then two huge and tawny bulks came into view. They were wild boars who had no doubt just crossed the river. As I stealthily approached I found them busily engaged in rooting up the heavy mulch of oak leaves around one of my prize lavender azaleas. Apparently they did not see me, hear me or catch my scent on the wind.

I backtracked to the house as fast as I could, got my high-powered .22 rifle and returned to the scene. The big brutes were still engaged in their bulldozing operations. I felt reasonably sure that

I could kill one of them but I wanted both. Such creatures are dangerous, and the damage they can do to a garden is in perfect proportion to their size and natural meanness.

I shot one, striking him farther back than I had intended. The other, panicked by the sound of the shot, started toward me, running like a scared hyena. I shot him also, but neither boar went down. I gave each a second shot, then a third, and that ended the business. I summoned some of the Negroes, and there was great rejoicing as I turned over 600 pounds of wild boar to them. And it was not yet sunrise on that placid plantation morning.

The great dramas of history that have been enacted in this area, and the vestiges of them in the old homes and buildings, make the spirit of the past ever present here. We cannot help but share the land with our ancestors.

Barely two miles from my plantation home is the old St. James Parish Church. An impressive piece of Georgian architecture, it has been there since 1768. Once it had a large congregation of planters, but since the disappearance of the rice it has stood empty except for one day a year in spring when we have a service there. On that

Old St. James Parish Church

The River, Looking Toward the Delta

occasion former parishioners and their descendants come thronging from distances up to three hundred miles. They all bring hampers packed with dinners, and the gathering is social as well as religious. Friends and relatives who do not see one another through the year meet once again.

Often after the religious service is over, and after the dinner and the attendant gossiping are concluded, I wait until the last guest has gone. I am alone with the beautiful and ancient church, now a sign and a symbol of what once was, and now a part also of the gentle and beautiful wildwood. Since I live closer to it than any other parishioner, I have long had nominal charge of it. For a building so old, that has been through earthquake and hurricane and cyclone, that has been the grave and patient witness of so many changes and chances of mortal life, it is remarkably preserved.

Undisturbed by the gay annual gathering, the men and women of an earlier day rest in the churchyard: the bloods of race track, card table and dueling field, the beauties of many a reception, many a dance, many a love affair. They all have fallen asleep, but in their silence they are still a part of the land.

My mind reverts to the early days when General Francis Marion and Colonel Banastre Tarleton fought a desperate skirmish within sight of this church. I think of the coming of Lord Rawdon and Major Fraser of the British army and, later, after peace had been won, of Washington and his party visiting the South for the first time, no doubt pausing to admire the architecture of the ancient church that had resisted so well the wilderness from which it had been wrested.

There are people who believe life on a plantation in the Deep South consists mainly of joyous lethargy and almost endless siestas, interrupted only by the vast effort of reaching for another julep. You have my word for it that this fancied tempo of life is far from accurate. Plantation life is exciting all year long. The changing year touches Hampton Plantation and its surrounding miles of wild country with a strong and varying hand. The mighty Santee River, the lonely green wilderness of the delta, the treacherous swamps infested with reptiles and alligators and the romantic ruins of deserted plantations afford forever-new experience.

There is a yearly pageant of adventure in this world around Hampton, and I would like to share it with others.

# SPRING

# A Satanic Jaunt

THE PLUTO OF HELL HOLE, that primeval region which surrounds Satan Swamp, is Ned Port. When he called out an invitation to me one day in late spring, I could hear the promise of adventure in his voice. "Bring your dogs over next Saturday. We're goin' to try to kill the ol' boar of Satan Swamp."

"I'll be over, Ned," I assured my ancient, grizzled friend. "Remember not to shoot me for a revenue officer when you see me coming."

Early that memorable Saturday morning I

rousted out a party of Negro helpers and then went to fetch my pack of dogs. Ranter, my leader, was eager for a hunt and he was enthusiastically supported by Yelping Maid and Gleeboy. I was eager myself and I wasted little time in getting our party organized.

Steve, in charge of the helpers, was mounted on his mule, Emma, while Paris and Anchovy walked. From home it is about six miles to the borders of Hell Hole. Steve and I decided to go by the road and take the dogs with us. Paris and Anchovy were to cut through the woods and meet us at Ned Port's still.

As Steve was about to get Emma under way, a task of no small proportions, we heard a voice behind us calling. It was Amnesia, Steve's much larger and better half. At her commanding tone, Emma relaxed comfortably while Steve sat up uncomfortably.

"What that woman want now?" he grumbled.

Down the road from her cabin hurried Amnesia. Emma batted back one ear. She had long since recognized the source of most of her master's trouble.

Amnesia nodded pleasantly enough to me, but her attitude toward Steve was militant. "You goin' for hunt. Well an' good. But we ain't got nothin' in the house for eat. Now, 'member, you ain't goin' for hunt fun—you goin' for hunt dinner. Either bring home that hog, or find some home an' woman where you can live 'thout work and 'thout eat. Is you understan' me, Steve?"

"I understan' you, Amnesia," Steve said, "but you just 'member that wild boar ain't so easy for ketch. He kin run like the debbil, and if he done make a stan', he have tush in his head sharp as a razor at a frolic. You ain't want that boar hog kill me, is you?"

"Not 'zactly," Amnesia admitted grudgingly as she turned back toward the house. "Least way, not 'fore you done brung him home."

This parting shot did not leave my dusky hench-man in a happy mood. Sawing with the rope lines to get Emma into action, he called to the hounds. Together we set off down the dewy morning road, flanked on either hand by endless reaches of glim-mering pine timber. Steve was silent for a long time, and I did not break in on his meditations until we were halfway to Ned's place.

"Amnesia is very much in earnest about your bringing her some bacon," I ventured.

"If I ketch the boar, an' the sow all two, same-fashion all the pig, Amnesia wouldn' satisfy. Cap'n, is you know when a woman is satisfy right?"

I confessed ignorance on this vital matter.

"She satisfy," said Steve, with the melancholy certainty that comes only from experience, "when she got a man an' got him scared."

Having delivered this weighty pronouncement, Steve smote Emma with both his heels for emphasis. Emma's only response was a slight twitching of her patient tail.

"In that case," I said, "Amnesia ought to be satisfied with you, Steve."

"Cap'n, you don' know Amnesia," he answered profoundly.

Leaving the main road we struck through the margins of Hell Hole—the strange, wild region of virgin forest, where gigantic pines climb the sky and are pulled back to earth by gigantic vines; where stretch many miles of shimmering greenery spotted by gleaming, dark red swamp water; a region of beauty and silence, of immediate stillness and far cries, of mystery and solitude.

It was late spring, and the forest was under-bedded with a lush growth of magic-looking ferns, green gallberries and waving broom sedge. We passed a thicket, a riotous canopy of May foliage, which I knew contained a hidden clear space near the ground. The fragrant sweet gums in the thicket

*32*

had two or three tiers of dry limbs, deadened by lack of sunlight, and on an earlier trip I had discovered that this shaded pocket was the haven of a family of wild turkeys.

Hell Hole is a perfect abode for wild life—deer, turkeys, foxes, wild hogs and an occasional black bear. Until you have been in a place like it, you have not come rightly to understand the fascination of the Low Country of the Carolinas. And until you see the pack of a pinelander like my friend Ned Port, you have never rightly understood dogs.

Our approach to Ned's woodland abode was suddenly interrupted by a furious attack from the roadside bushes made by one of his curs on the innocent Emma. Emma sidled, bided her time and then implanted on the eager face of the intruder such a kick as I had never seen executed on any gridiron. The dog hobbled away into the bushes, his interest in the matter of biting mules gone.

Coming from under a dense canopy of live-oak limbs that were heavy with packed foliage and bannering moss, we saw Ned's place and Ned himself, standing by the gate, dressed for the woods and the hunt. Ned is normally dressed for the

*Will, a Fine Hunter*

woods, but when he has hunting guests he does his company the honor of wearing his grandfather's hunting horn.

This horn never amuses me except when Ned wears it. It is too big for him. When you see it on him, in fact, you hardly know which one is wearing the other. Ned's grandfather was a regular giant, and his hunting equipment ran to things Gargantuan. This horn, I have heard, came from an oversized steer of the Texas long-horned breed. With it on, Ned looks as ridiculous as a flivver equipped with tractor tires.

He met us with a quiet smile. "Is them dogs any account?" he asked with that refreshing ingenuousness that a woodlander is likely to have. He indicated my pack—Ranter, Yelping Maid and Gleeboy—at the same time casting a look of satisfied appraisal toward his own prides and joys beside him. A rangy, mangy, piratic crew they looked, as if the ethnic pot had run over and spilled some scum.

"What do you call them, Ned?" I asked, knowing well his love for appropriate and picturesque names.

"That pair," he said, pointing to two dogs of an undetermined breed, "I call them Smut and Smoke. This one lying here is Jailbird. That's

Angel by the fence there—she that's got the tail bit off and the frazzled ear what a wildcat chewed; and yonder by the house are the best of all, Do and Don't. You see," Ned explained, "one of 'em is always right about a trail, and if one won't ketch a hog or steer the other will."

"I see," I admitted, making a mental note that every human being should have a pair of helpers of some sort that would act in the perfect concert of Do and Don't.

"I brought Steve with me," I said, indicating my dozing rider on his dozing mule, "and I have Paris Green and Anchovy coming through the woods. They'll be here soon."

Ned smiled again. "They been here a long time," he said. "My wife done give 'em breakfast in the kitchen. They're sleepin' in the sun by the barn now."

After some effort we waked our huntsmen, Paris and Anchovy. Then, with Ned, his pack and Old Testament, we hied us into the lustrous, glimmering heart of Hell Hole, toward that bourn of the forbidding name—Satan Swamp.

"How about this wild boar, Ned?" I asked my host. "Is he still as wild and mean as you thought he was last year when he got away from you?"

Like a true woodsman, Ned considered his answer before he spoke. Any honest sportsman is grave when he talks of dangerous game. "I didn't make no mistake," he said. "This is the boar that killed them two fine hounds what Mr. Hutchins paid fifty dollars apiece for. This is the same hog that cut up Ephraim Garrett that lives down the road here. One of his little dogs cornered it, and he went in on it like a fool, and the boar ripped both his legs wide open."

I glanced surreptitiously at my henchmen to see the effect of this story on them. Paris had not heard it, but Anchovy's eyes were bulging and had in them the telltale light of panic. Steve feigned indifference, but I could see him kicking Emma nervously, and he muttered to himself—a sure sign he was getting uneasy.

As for Old Testament, he tucked in the ragged fringe of his shirt and gave his trousers a hitch, fastening them more tightly with a stick thrust through a buttonhole. His general air, though, seemed to me that of an athlete stripped for the course rather than that of a warrior girding for battle.

"I see this boar last week," Ned told me as all the huntsmen, fascinated, closed ranks to listen, "and he was walkin' along on that high ridge in Satan Swamp just like nobody's business.

"His tushes are long as your white hound's tail and have just about the same curl in 'em, and sharp! You remember that long knife what Judge Seabrook had 'em show in court the time they tried Snake Wiley for killin' Jim Hampson? You remember how he made ribbons out of Jim—regular streamers? That's how sharp this boar's tushes are."

"Well," spoke up Paris, "if I can help myself this day, I ain't goin' give him no chance to kill no man. Far as I concern, he ain't goin' kill no man. I'se rather go hungry than have a hog big as a mule . . ."

"Big as a mule?" Old Testament broke in scornfully. "Boy, what you talkin' 'bout? This boar stan' higher than Emma."

At this, Steve pulled Emma up short—which was fine with her, because she was especially good at stopping and standing. "Hog tall as Emma?" Steve asked in a whisper. The thing had seized his imagination.

"If he ever git a man on them tush, he'll wave him roun' same like them school chillun wave them flag."

"Same fashion," Old Testament confirmed fervently.

Paris' reference to waving flags registered painfully with Anchovy. The fact that he had on a red and white shirt no doubt provided excellent tinder for his imagination, suggesting to him that the great boar of Hell Hole might make a nice distinction and choose his man for artistic rather than for personal reasons. You could almost see the idea grow in his mind. Suddenly, feigning extreme warmth, Anchovy hunched out of the flaming shirt and craftily tied it behind the wreck of wood and leather that Steve called a saddle. "Ain't goin' to wave me," he muttered. "How he goin' to wave me? Ain't I got two foot? Is I goin' to have pyralysis and stan' like I was nail on the groun'?"

Ned, who was heading our procession, suddenly stopped, and the Negroes were struck motionless in mid-step. Their eyes searched the heavy woods for places of retreat and exit. I must confess I gave a little jump myself.

"The place is right yonder," Ned said, pointing to a deep and most mysterious part of the general wilderness. "Right by that bunch of pines yonder that we call Seven Sisters is where Dead Man's Ridge begins."

Steve, Paris, Anchovy and Old Testament looked at one another significantly. Anchovy, even without his shirt, was perspiring freely.

"It was right off there that Ephraim Garrett

got cut to pieces," Ned told us, as if he were a realtor recounting the pleasant traditions of the place. "Down that abandoned road to the right is the spot where Old Man Cain shot his wife and mother-in-law to death."

"Why he shoot he wife?" whispered Paris.

"They say he didn' know what else to do with her," Old Testament answered.

"Come on, boys," Ned said, suddenly abandoning his reflections. "We're pretty close to the fun now. Hold up!" He pointed to the wet sand in the road. "There's the track of that killer right now. Here," he commanded. "Look at this if you want to see a real hog track."

Deeply impressed were the prints of a gigantic hog. It seemed to me, indeed, that they might be those of a heifer or a young bull; but I did not want to question Ned's word.

"What you think, Steve?" asked Old Testament, a certain pride tinging his tone.

"That may be a hog," Steve admitted, "but he ain't no hog for ketch."

"He meat would be mighty tough," quoth Anchovy, hoping for retreat.

"They don' grow that way back home," Paris said thoughtfully, "but if he git ketch—my Jehovah, what a ham!"

At this heartening observation there was some licking of lips, and it seemed to me that the morale of our party went up a little.

"I think," said Ned, "that we'll make a start right here."

A little to my surprise Ned solemnly unslung his mighty hunting horn and began to sound it like the blast of doom. At the sound Smut and Smoke, Do and Don't, Yelping Maid, Gleeboy and all the other hounds began to howl amiably and miserably, as if the citadels of their souls were being overrun by angelic devils. Some of them sat down, striking the classic pose for this mournful rite. Gleeboy by mischance sat suddenly on a sharp stick, and his quick, unabashed yelp jarred on the grieving harmony of the wailing chorus.

"A horn gits to a hound," Ned said rather breathlessly, "and makes him think of bigger game than fleas. We'll turn 'em loose on the trail right here."

"How are we going to follow them, Ned? Have any set plan?" I asked.

"We scatter out through the woods hereabouts, and when the dogs round up the old boar and bring him to bay, why, the nearest one to him goes in on him."

"Saviour in Heaven!" cried out Steve. "What

you mean, Cap'n Ned, when you say, 'Goes in on him'?"

"I mean go for him, jump on him, throw him down and hold him til the rest of us git there."

Steve grinned in an abashed way as if Ned were honoring him too highly.

"A local man," he observed sagely, "like Old Testament here, ought surely go in on him first."

"That so," Anchovy chimed in.

"He say," Paris added, "that we is to scatter 'bout in the woods. I'm thinkin' I is better at scatterin' than at goin' in."

"Put them dogs on the trail and let's ketch this killer," said Ned with assumed testiness. "If you boys is so scared of a hog, I wonder what you'd do if the dogs happened to find an ol' b'ar."

"I ain't lost no b'ar," said Anchovy quickly.

By this time the dogs had begun to trail off into the bushes, yowling out the sweet tidings that they had settled to a trail that was a trail. Yet no one, not even the hounds themselves, dreamed that our tremendous game was so close. Even while we were gingerly and, with remarkable tenacity for one another's company, tentatively "scattering," two hundred yards ahead of us in the heart of a dense thicket of sweet myrtle and smilax vines a bomb exploded. Some monstrous thing started a mighty rush through the tangled greenery, while the dogs in full cry let us know that the boar was up and on his way.

A glance at our Negroes showed the four of them standing so close that they seemed welded together.

"Yonder he goes!" shouted Ned excitedly, pointing toward a high open ridge. Down it raced a gray shape of formidable size and cyclone speed.

Here was no mere wild hog, but a true wild boar of savage aspect and awesome proportions. Here, indeed, within our sight, was the killer of Satan Swamp.

"Come on! Come on!" cried Ned. "They'll bring him to bay, and we ought to be up with 'em. Hey, what're you all standin' there like that for?"

Reluctantly the four came toward us.

"Cap'n," said Steve soberly, "we done see that thing, an' we don' think we can ketch that hog."

"If the dog can ketch him, well an' good," Paris explained, as if he did not wish completely to back down, "but if they have a bad luck, we ought ketch somethin' else."

"Cap'n Ned, ain't you got no smaller hog in these woods?" asked Anchovy. "If the dogs can't specify with a hog, how can man specify?"

To these queries Ned's only reply was a triumphant, "They've got him now! Now's our chance!"

Toward the far-off melee we ran, through bunches of huckleberry bushes, over old logs, down long yellow savannas of broom grass. We were making so much noise ourselves that we could not tell by the sounds ahead just what was happening in our van. The Negroes kept very close behind us but were by no means eager to pass. They kept close to one another also, running almost as one man. Even Old Testament, the senior of the other three by many years, was right with them.

Our first intimation of how the battle was going came with dramatic suddenness. We did not come to something, however—something came to us. Before us the bushes parted wildly, and toward us rushed a frantically demoralized pack. I could not at first distinguish how many dogs there were, but it looked like most of them and they were scared to death. They took scurrying refuge behind us and began whining, whimpering and licking their wounds.

Ned turned to examine their injuries, and I looked to the wounded courage of my huntsmen.

"We didn't get up in time," I explained.

Steve laughed a laugh of unrelieved terror. "The dogs git there in time," he said, "an' look what done happen to them."

"What's the next move, Ned?" I asked.

"My dog Angel ain't come back," he said, "and I can't hear her bayin'."

Anchovy began to snicker. "She's sure bayin' a angel song 'bout now, Cap'n."

"Let's get to where they bayed him," Ned proposed.

Forward we went, all of us sharing to some degree a general uneasiness. The dogs followed us tentatively, seeming to marvel at our boldness, and their looks were not lost on our helpers.

"When I look at Gleeboy," Anchovy remarked, "he done seem to say, 'You goin' pretty fas' an' happy to be goin' where you is goin'.'"

"Yes," Paris agreed, "we start out with a dog we call Don't an' now we has a whole pack Don't."

Ned, leading our not over-valiant van, came to a halt on the pine ridge ahead of us, and we saw him gazing ruefully at something. As we came up we saw that it was all that was left of Angel.

"She's done been made a flag of," Steve commented.

"Now," said Ned, "here's another reason why this killer's got to die. It ain't lettin' no boar kill my best dog for nothing."

"That's so," Old Testament agreed.

"You feel that way, Cap'n Ned," Steve ventured, "but kin we git them dogs to join in that feelin'?"

To my surprise the pack returned to the trail, but dutifully rather than enthusiastically. They headed for the darksome, haunted borders of Satan Swamp. We followed, some of us vengefully and some of us because we didn't care to be left behind.

Down Dead Man's Ridge we went, the dogs warming to the trail, and suddenly we came to Bloody Creek—a deep woodland watercourse, appropriately named for the leaf-stained color of its mysterious water. We had to hunt for a ford and eventually found an old animal crossing. There was a considerable bluff on the opposite side, and in this there was a small aperture—evidently the opening of a cave.

On the sand bar Steve spotted tracks that he took for those of a possum. They led to the cave's mouth. Here, indeed, was rare good fortune. Was not this a chance to appease Amnesia without having to face the dreadful killer? While the dogs

crossed the creek and trailed into a little thicket,
Steve followed the possum to his lair. Coming to
the opening, he paused to consider. His hesitation
earned him the sarcasm of his fellows.

"Let me hol' your hat," volunteered Anchovy.

"Gimme them pants, Steve. You ain't goin'
need them no more."

"Buryin' you ain't goin' cost Amnesia a cent.
You done been real considerate an' die in a hole
that's already done dig."

"Steve," whined Old Testament, "don't forgit
to say your prayers, boy, 'fore you go in that
place."

Steve would never have gone, but he had nicely
estimated the odds. If he could get a possum he
would be safely heeled. It would be far safer to
"go in on" a sleeping possum than to go in on a
ramping wild boar, his tusks still bloody from
recent execution.

We gathered around the cave's opening while
Steve crawled through. Inside, he complained that
he could not see very clearly and asked us to stand
away from the mouth so as not to cut off the light.
He groped his way back into the dark hole after
the possum.

Meanwhile, things of a wild and confused nature began to happen. First we heard the dogs

in the dense thicket up on the creek bank begin a frantic outcry. There was a rocking of bush tops, sounds of a desperate rush, a sudden lull. Then, sliding and plunging down the creek bank not twenty yards from us came the killer himself. Close behind him was the yelping, bawling, whining pack, apparently emboldened by the fact that they seemed to have their enemy on the run.

The fugitive slid to the sandbank bordering the bed of the creek and paused for a bickering moment—head high, bristles up, tail up. He champed his jaws in slantwise fashion. Then he saw us and came head on. But he was suddenly reminded of the dogs, who now came in a huddling gang to the top of the slide above him. I saw the boar cut his little fierce eyes upward toward his pursuers, who all at once seemed none too certain of the wisdom of their course.

In the excitement of the moment I had failed to take note of the effect of the boar's coming on my huntsmen. Now I looked for them, and Ned alone stood by my side. "Look out!" I heard him say sharply. "He's comin' for us!"

When a wild boar means mischief he makes his run with his head down. It is by a sudden thrust upward of his tusks that he does his deadly work. When he charges with his head high he probably

A Hunter's Boat in the Rice Fields

means that he just wants gangway. This beast charged us with his head up and he did not come all the way. Suddenly he turned abruptly toward the opening of the little cave into which Steve had gone, possum-bent. The boar plunged toward it with a rickety, veering rush.

"My Gawd!" yelled Ned. "He gone after Steve!"

To do him justice, Ned was steady of nerve.

49

He too made a break for the gloomy aperture. As I followed I thought how treacherous all caves look with their gaping jaws.

The boar reached the opening first and tried to dash inside. He was rather too big for such a doorway and he did not have time to examine it. After a confused moment Ned and I found ourselves trying to hold the boar, while he, half inside and half outside, was frantically trying to kick loose. I had one of his big feet a dozen times, but he always knocked me loose. Ned had a gallant grip on his tail.

It was a silent struggle. As a rule when a hog squeals he is beginning to admit defeat. This boar hadn't begun to fight. The dogs meanwhile had halted at some distance behind us and were giving a few feeble yaps. They seemed more than willing for us to finish the job.

Despite the intensity of the struggle there was practically no sound, so that when we suddenly heard a subterranean voice from the darkness of the cave it sounded like thunder.

"Who done darken that door?" Steve complained. "Ain't I done ask you all don' darken that door?"

Ned shouted, partly to Steve but mostly to the

wide, wide world, "If this boar's tail pops you'll know what darken that door!"

"Ned," I gasped, "where are all the others? If we had them we could hold this thing."

"I reckon they been home for some time," he answered. Then, "Oh, my gosh!"

The boar's flight had really never been delayed by me. Ned had held him manfully until his tail, probably weakened by some old wound, pulled off. Into the darkness and into Steve the monster plunged.

We stood aside to give Steve a clear track. I was looking for him but I didn't see much of him. A streaming meteor shot by us—a projectile that as far as I could tell hurricaned straight past without once touching the ground.

There was a big, bare sweet gum tree on the far side of the creek, and toward this Steve instinctively sped. All in one motion it seemed, he took the wide dark creek, caught one of the higher limbs of the gum and made a giant swing to safety. Then he scuttled upward like a frantic squirrel.

Ned and I then discovered that this same tree was literally draped with brave Killer-killers. Ensconced there, thirty feet from the ground, was Anchovy. Six feet higher, tightly wedged in a crotch, sat Paris. Thirty feet higher, stretched out on a limb like a black fox squirrel, lay Old Testament. He didn't want that boar even to see him—crafty old man!

"Come on down here, you buzzards!" yelled Ned. "Ain't no bacon up there."

"Cap'n," called Steve, "kin you block up that hole I done left open just now?"

Our pack had meanwhile utterly lost interest in the chase. They were lolling about, idly licking their wounds, lapping up water and giving fleas the bum's rush.

Ned and I together carried an old log and thrust it into the cave's opening. At sight of the barricade our henchmen began warily to clamber down the gum tree. Gingerly they came over to where Ned and I stood on the sand bar.

"We've got him now," said Ned. "All we have to do is go in on him."

"That's all," I confirmed lightly, in a tone intended to convey simple manliness and confidence.

Steve, Paris, Anchovy and Old Testament looked at one another. There was unanimity in their glance, but not the stuff of which heroes are made.

"Are you ready?" asked Ned, taking a step toward the cave.

"Cap'n Ned, you'll have to 'scuse us this time," Paris said. "Steve an' me an' Anchovy done have a meetin' of the Sons of Pharaoh's Daughter on Tuesday night, an' we can't miss that."

"No, sah!" the other two chimed in.

"How about you, old man?" asked Ned, turning to Old Testament. "You scared too?"

"I ain't scare," he protested, "but I done promise my wife Neuralgia I won' go in no scare place."

Ned looked at me in despair. "You and I'll go in," he said. "We'll show these triflin' no-goods how to act."

Once more we advanced on the cave. With caution Ned and I lifted away the blocking log. Glancing behind me I saw our four men backing away toward the creek.

Ned stooped to peer into the darkness of the cavern. Weirdly, with silent speed, a great gray shape suddenly filled the opening.

"Look out!" yelled Ned, making a break for it.

I clambered up the bank with an ease and a spirit that amazed me. By the time I looked around, the charging boar was nowhere in sight, but every Negro was perched in the tall gum tree exactly as he had been before. And next to Old Testament was Ned himself! We exchanged shamefaced grins—he from the tree and I from the bank.

After this collapse of our morale we called off the hunt, collected all the dogs but Angel, corralled Emma and started homeward.

# The Lilies of Tarleton's Deep

My near neighbors, the men of the wilderness, had told him very plainly that if he came back into Tabor Swamp they would kill him. Old Ben Burley told him so, and all the men of the Burley clan had seconded their leader's threat. Into the wild and melancholy domain of these fierce men Congaree had followed one of his stray cattle; when the swamp men had come on him searching, they had summarily issued their warning. Without reply, Congaree had desisted from his search and returned to his humble home.

"I ain't meant no harm," he kept saying to himself, as if mildly justifying his having visited the swamp that lay northward from his tiny clearing on the brink of the vast sea marshes. "I ain't meant no harm," he repeated aloud; and then over and over he kept puzzling in his mind what he had overheard Ben Burley mutter to himself: "We are in big trouble out here, and we don't want no strangers prowling round."

What could that trouble be? On the faces of the men who had driven him out Congaree had seen stamped a great fear. Perhaps, he thought, the men of Tabor Swamp had good cause for telling him to clear out. The whole business seemed mysterious, dangerous.

And it was. Indeed, the affair was heartbreaking. It involved all the Tabors and the Burleys and the Minots—the three families, closely related by marriage, who owned or controlled the immense tract of semi-wasteland known as Tabor Swamp. On all of them a strange and deep trouble had suddenly fallen. And the big trouble that Congaree puzzled over was the disappearance of Rosalie Burley.

The tiny golden-haired daughter of Ben Burley, a child not quite three years old, had vanished from her home far back in the Tabor Swamp woods. Since it was March, when the first white lilies of the forest bloom, she might have gone down the path from her home toward the edges of the deep swamp. Her father had shown her some lily buds near the spring there. It was on that pathway that she had last been seen on Tuesday evening. It was Wednesday forenoon when the swamp men encountered Congaree. They were searching for the lost child, and their dispositions, always proud and sensitive, were on a desperate edge. These rough and hulking woodsmen loved Rosalie with a fierce tenderness. To them "Rosalie" was a fit name for the child whose wild-rose loveliness reminded them of happy flowers. As nothing else could, she inspired their deepest love, and as nothing else could, her disappearance roused them to a pitch of wild and incredible dismay.

When Wednesday afternoon came, and their careful search of the swamp had proved fruitless, the men held a solemn council. At this Ben Burley presided.

"She's gone," he said bluntly. "We can't find her. All we got is the little blue ribbon that was hanging on the myrtle bush. What can we do now, boys? We can't give her up."

"The little blue ribbon," muttered one of the

*The Rosebud Orchid,* Cleistes divaricata

men desolately, "and the tracks in the sand by the spring."

"Do you think, Cousin Ben," asked tall, spare hawkeyed Jim Tabor—"do you think anybody could have kidnaped Rosalie? She was pretty enough," he ended with mournful emphasis.

That dreadful word *kidnaped* was a foreign one to the remote community of Tabor Swamp; but the suggestion took hold of the wary, anxious and baffled party of men.

"Only rich people get their children stole," Ben Burley objected. "Ain't none of us rich," he added with decision.

"But, Cousin Ben, you was mighty rich in having Rosalie," Jim Tabor suggested.

"Anybody would want to have her, same like we do," another member of the group said.

"Hold on now," spoke out old Amos Burley in his slow, authoritative voice. "Didn't we run that Congaree out of here yesterday? What was he doing away over here on our side of the swamp? What kind of a man is he, anyhow?"

"He's the only stranger who's been here in a month," Dick Minot put in.

"Don't nobody know just who that fellow is," old Amos continued. "He just dropped down into this country and took over Sambo's deserted place on Owendaw Creek. Those boats that take the inside passage come right by his door, and he sells to strangers," he ended.

"What if this Congaree is our man?" Jim Tabor asked sternly, his gray eyes glittering beneath his shaggy eyebrows. "He might steal the child for somebody else—gypsies or tourists or the like."

To Jim, and to all other members of the clan, people not within the circles of their families were strangers and liable to suspicion. Even Congaree, though he had been at Owendaw for six years, was a stranger to them. He lived outside the swamp and was not a Burley, a Minot or a Tabor.

"Amos and Jim, they done struck the trail," growled Asher Minot, a huge, bearlike man, black-bearded, deep-voiced and menacing of aspect.

"I think you're right," Ben Burley blurted out. "Congaree lives right by the creek where all those houseboats pass. He has dealings with strangers. He sells them things."

"Are we ready to start?" asked young Dick Minot sharply.

"We're ready," Jim Tabor answered. "It's six miles by the road but not half of that straight through the swamp."

"We'll be going," said Ben Burley with grim decision.

"Congaree will tell us," the formidable Asher

Minot muttered. "We'll get it out of him."

Thus it was that eleven men set forth on the dusky pathways of Tabor Swamp, their goal the humble cabin of Congaree.

Between Congaree's house—huddled obscurely under a great live oak which overhung Owendaw Creek—and the Tabor Swamp, there was a wide reach of melancholy marshland—a waste of reedy morasses, treacherous bogs and whispering stretches of mazy sedges. Beyond the cabin lay the creek, a deep tidal estuary which formed a part of the inland waterway system along the lonely coast; then sea marsh, glimmering and still; then the ocean. A solitary place it was, and Congaree lived alone. Yet sometimes the passing craft stopped at his staggering wharf and there took on fresh water and, occasionally, such vegetables as the Negro's tiny garden would supply.

It was after two o'clock in the afternoon when the men of Tabor Swamp set out for Congaree's home. Just then he was entertaining an old acquaintance, Bram Jackson. Congaree was quietly recounting his recent experience in the swamp. Bram's eyes grew wide with fear. Before his friend had completed his story, Bram drew from his pocket a tiny calico sunbonnet. It was torn and crushed.

"I find this in the swamp," Bram said. "I been

after a wild turkey. Don' this belong to a chil'?"

Congaree looked grave. Was this the deep trouble of which Ben Burley had spoken?

"I hear that a little chil' lost in the swamp," Bram went on. "Maybe this is her hat," he suggested, holding up the pathetic thing. One of the blue ribbons was missing.

"You is a fool to carry it with you if you look like that," said Congaree bluntly. "Folk'll think you know something about this chil'. Where'd you find it?" he demanded.

"Right back here on Hickory Ridge."

"Today?"

"This mornin'. Congaree, I must be goin' now. I better leave this hat here. I might meet somebody."

"Leave it," said Congaree in a tone which had a depth of meaning Bram could not fathom. Taking the tiny relic he laid it on a bench beside him on the porch. "I'll take it to Mr. Burley tomorrow," he said.

"You better not!" exclaimed Bram, his eyes filled with apprehension.

Congaree looked at him coldly. "A man," he said, "better always do what he oughter do."

Bram did not answer, but from his shifty step and furtive look it was clear that he was a believer in always doing the easy and politic thing. He was anxious to be gone.

When Bram left, the sun was two hours high. Congaree glanced appraisingly at it. Then he gazed thoughtfully toward Tabor Swamp.

"They should know about this little bonnet tonight," he reasoned. "I'll drive in my cows from the marsh. Then I'll go."

Southward down a bypath from his cabin turned Congaree. The sunlight flickering on him through the live oaks highlighted his strong frame, his erect and manly bearing. A quiet independence showed in his alert and easy step. Such was Congaree, the man whom the dwellers in Tabor Swamp believed had stolen away their exquisite little sweetheart.

Almost as soon as the Negro had rounded the first bend in the marsh pathway he began to call up his cattle. Plaintive, soft, far-reaching was his call, as though he were singing his herd homeward with a lullaby. Congaree's call was answered by the secret birds of the marsh and by an ancient owl sequestered in the moldering swamp.

On went the Negro, along brackish rivulets, by tall ranks of whispering sedge, following the winding cattle track. At last he heard a cow low, and soon he came within sight of a greedy old Jer-

*The Marshes*

sey up to her knees in mud, gathering with her curling tongue the succulent tops of the young marsh which was just beginning to spring. But his other two cows Congaree could not see.

"I wonder now," he mused, going forward slowly and examining the tracks in the damp sand. "I wonder if them other ones . . ."

Suddenly the Negro caught his breath. Then he eased himself down on one knee to gaze at a footprint, a tiny one—and of a kind that he had never seen in the marsh before.

"A little chil'," he said, rising and looking about him. "She ain't been gone long from here."

Again the Negro called; and after that he shaded his eyes with his hand and looked across a very peculiar stretch of sand. It had been carefully fenced off from the marshland proper. Congaree and the other men whose stock ranged on this reedy moor had united in building the fence.

Up and down the coast the stretch was known as Tarleton's Deep. Since Revolutionary days a legend had persisted that three of Tarleton's roving cavalrymen had gone down in this dreadful pit—half quagmire, half quicksand, and most dangerous. In it grew certain fair flowers: wild flags, wampee, water lilies and white lilies. Its moisture, coming from the swamp rather than from the sea, was fresh, and the vivid greenness of the water plants growing in it had often lured cattle into its grasp. Then the fence had been built, and Congaree, as the man who lived nearest, kept it in repair. Near the north end he always had in readiness a small roll of barbed wire.

It was along the north side of the fence that Congaree had come, and again he paused to call and to look for the mysterious tiny footprints.

Hardly had he given his first mellow whoop when behind him he heard someone running rapidly. He turned and saw a small child struggling through the fence fifty yards away. Now, with baby arms extended, she was running toward Tarleton's Deep and the white lilies she loved. Already she was on the very brink. Toward the quicksands and death Rosalie ran.

"Congaree! Congaree!" a frightened voice yelled to him from behind. "Run for you' life! Them men is at you' house right now! Ain't you done leave the little hat on the piazza? They'll git you! Run, Congaree!"

Shouting his warning, Bram Jackson passed Congaree like a storm. Whirling away down the marsh path, he turned a bend by some cedars and vanished into the swamp. Congaree heard the rising of an angry tumult. He knew that in a few moments, taking his track, the men would be on him. The Negro looked toward the child. "She's goin' to sink an' drown," he said simply.

Then, with a swiftness directed by a sudden and importunate purpose, he ran along outside the fence and reached a roll of rusty wire. He jerked the end free, stooped through the fence with it, raveled it until he had a long stretch free, then took a turn with it around a post. Grasping the other end he ran after the imperiled child. The wire tore Congaree's hand, but he paid no attention. Unless he had the wire both rescued and rescuer would surely sink in Tarleton's Deep. He was close to Rosalie.

The child was among the lilies, so intent on their beauty and on gathering two great lustrous ones that she did not realize she was sinking. Yet the sands had her. Already they were up to her knees.

Amid beauty, amid the marsh stillness, in the quiet evening the monster of Tarleton's Deep laid its fearful claim on Rosalie. In the ancient swamp through which she had come there had been no danger to compare with this. But Congaree was near.

"Don' you be afraid," he said gently, apprehensive lest she try to run, and in struggling sink

The Sinister Pitcher Plants

deeper. "You pa's lookin' for you. You jus' let me carry you out of the water."

Congaree himself was now deep in the quagmire. He had shifted the wire to his left hand. Struggling forward, he reached far out with his right to grasp the child. His footing suddenly seemed to go from under him. He sank almost to his waist in the chill and eager sands. Rosalie, too, was fast sinking, but now Congaree's strong arm went around her. Out of Tarleton's Deep he lifted her.

Holding the child carefully, he began to pull himself painfully out of the grip of the quagmire. His hand torn and bleeding, his strength waning, knowing that the worst danger would have to be faced when the men from Tabor Swamp appeared, Congaree toiled on.

When Congaree had almost reached the fence a group of eleven frantic men came rushing down the path. Old Ben Burley was in the lead, and after him came gaunt Jim Tabor, Amos Burley, black-bearded Asher Minot and all the rest. Murderous vengeance was in their hearts and on their faces. In his right hand old Ben gripped his rifle. In the other, crushed with the strength of his despair, was Rosalie's sunbonnet. From his bronzed hand the blue ribbon dangled strangely. Dick

Minot, impetuous and wild, was shouting madly. They rushed toward Congaree.

The silent Negro, never pausing, reached one side of the fence just as the men reached the other. He lifted Rosalie gently across the barrier and laid her safely in her father's arms.

"I wanted more flowers," Rosalie explained, "but he carried me out of the water." She told them in her elfin fashion of her wanderings in the swamp, where she had slept, of finding the lilies.

One by one the men were convinced, and one by one to the tacit Congaree they came and solemnly shook his hand. When a swamp man does that, he pays a mighty tribute. And thus it was that Rosalie got the white lilies after all; and thus it was that the undying affection of the fierce clansmen of Tabor Swamp was won by Congaree.

# SUMMER

# Drama in Two Acts

THE GREAT diamondback rattlesnake lay under the green shade of the dense turkeyberry bushes that fringed the edge of the vast and lonely swamp. The July air was as clear as a perfect white jewel, with mists and faint hints of opaline light along the horizon. A light wind, blowing inland from the nearby sea, mingled the spicy odors of the far salt marshes and cedar groves with the hushed and aromatic fragrance of the pines.

On three sides rose the mighty pines, and to the westward, as if marginal to lands of mystery and

wonder, loomed shadowy cypresses in the solemn
sorrow of perpetual mourning. The underbrush
in the woods was not high but it afforded thick
cover. Here and there a sultry red orchis, dreamy
and Oriental, or a cool blue larkspur lightened
the prevailing green of the background. There
were huckleberries, too, hanging in indolent dim
clusters; gallberries twinkling in their dark, glossy
foliage like jet beads; and prickly pears with their
heavy, thorny leaves, their tawdry, flaming blossoms and their uninviting green fruit. It was shady
and cool under these bushes, a pleasant retreat
from the afternoon sun.

The big rattlesnake, however, was not at ease.
He had shed his skin the day before and had fool-
ishly crawled nearly half a mile in his new coat, following the elusive trail of a family of swamp rabbits. He was sore, irritable and wakeful. He lay
restless in a flat coil, his broad, malignant head
resting on a gray tuft of sphagnum moss, his tail,
with its triumph of sixteen rattles, moving nervously over a little space of white sand.

His gorgeous coat, black, brown and of a tawny
gold, with all the colors new and bright, was exquisite, but its charm was like the false lure of evil.
Six feet he measured from tip to tip—a diamondback of the swamps, the most venomous and the

most morose of all rattlesnakes. His baleful yellow eyes glittered in their shallow sockets. His head was broad and angular. His great body arched away from his head until it reached the size of a strong man's arm; there it tapered gradually to his blunt tail, tipped by the dry-whispering rattles.

Among the various forest tones there was a vibrating sound, the thud of a solitary woodman's ax ringing into the deep heart of a tall yellow pine that stood about thirty yards from where the snake lay.

The man had been at work on the tree since noon, and his relentless strokes were at last telling on the stately monarch. He was deep on the back cut now and he glanced about to see where he could run clear of the fall. There was an old sheep path through the turkeyberries, running at right angles to the proposed line of the cast, that looked best.

Presently he saw the crest of the pine shiver and sway. Then he heard a crack at the bottom and, grasping his ax by the hilt, he sprang lightly away down the blind path, looking back over his shoulder. The pine shuddered through all its splendid height, sank majestically from its lofty place in the blue heavens, whirled with gathering speed, spun on its axis and plunged straight down on the bewildered man. He had only time to turn with a smothered cry before a far-reaching limb struck him heavily to the earth.

The end of the limb drove itself deep into the ground just a few feet beyond the man, pinning him. His right arm was crushed close in to his body. His weight had fallen on his left elbow and his arm was broken near the shoulder. He fainted when he tried to move it.

When he opened his eyes a minute later, somewhat recovered from the first shock, only his will kept him from fainting again. For there, a scant two feet away, the great diamondback rattlesnake was poised ready to strike.

At the first downward rush of the tree the snake had turned in flight. But the violent fall of the man had seemed a threat of attack, and the snake had turned to fight.

The man knew rattlesnakes well enough to realize the delicacy of his situation. If he stirred—if he closed his eyes, perhaps—the reptile would strike him, full in the face most likely. The broken arm that he had tried to move caused him excruciating pain. He shifted it ever so softly, and the fierce, wide head shot down swiftly; but

76

it withdrew without striking, its eyes glittering.

Supreme upon the topmost bough of a near-by live oak, a joyous mockingbird sang a few cool notes to the crystal air; then, hearing the rattle-snake, he paused tremulously, turned his head to one side to make certain of his fear and flew wildly away. A shy wood thrush let his inquisi-tiveness lead him near the buzzing rattles; then he, too, darted away through the bush.

So the man and the reptile were left alone. The only sound was that of the insistent, cruel song of the rattles.

The agony of the woodsman's mind was clearly visible on his face, and the rattlesnake saw the change. The monstrous head drew back, flatten-ing. The rattles sang shrilly. And the man, his face bleak and gray, closed his eyes.

The rattles whirred wildly for a second. Then they ceased abruptly. There was a sound of scaly movement. The man's eyes opened on an amaz-ing sight. The great rattlesnake had dropped swiftly from his coil. Now he glided furtively by the man without even noticing him.

The man guessed what had frightened the snake, but because of the height of the bushes he did not see it until it was quite near. With a swift and rocking motion a king snake came hot on the rattler's trail. His bright eyes darted this way and that, glittering with the fierce love of battle. He made not a sound as he sped past.

His size was not so great as that of the rattlesnake but his skin was far more beautiful. Wide bands of pure black and white circled the muscular, lithe body, built for strangling, for his inveterate enemy.

The speed of this silent champion was wonderful. His graceful body swayed into curves that shot him forward along the thin paths through the underbrush. Near where the man lay he paused momentarily, glanced curiously at the pinioned form and darted silently on.

Struggling backward, the woodsman worked himself clear of the binding limb. He caught sight of two flashing bodies wrapped in gorgeous battle, swaying, struggling, twisting, strangling. The great thunderbolt had fallen on the rattler, and no rattler that ever grew would have been a match for him.

The woodsman ventured near and watched the end of the battle. In a few minutes the beautiful demon with the tawny coat of black and gold lay lifeless in the powerful coils of the king snake.

## Drama in Two Acts

So the man came home safely, except for his broken arm, and the rattlesnake died in fair battle with the king snake.

Countless white bubbles rose to the surface of the dark swamp water. The lily pads anchored by their long black stems slid softly back and forth on the surface, moved from the depths by some invisible power. Gradually among the bubbles there appeared what looked like a walnut floating in the water. Higher it rose, growing wider, more irregular. Two great eyes in protruding sockets cleared the level of the water, followed by the huge armored body of a bull alligator. Monstrous and scaly, looking like a dragon of medieval tapestry, he lay still in the mellow sunshine with his body half-submerged and his wicked head thrust partly up on a spongy grass tussock.

A gray squirrel, tail arched, barked at him from a cool retreat among the tender leaves of a sweet gum. A foolish bluejay that had been inspecting a pine sapling growing on the edge of the morass peered impudently at him, scolded him harshly, but suddenly grew afraid and flew away screaming. The blue and green dragonflies that could poise so jauntily on the sere reed tops whisked daringly over the drowsing alligator, flared in glittering circles above him and returned with defiant grace to their perches. Far up in the blue profound of the noonday sky a solitary osprey, which had a nest on the crest of the dead cypress that stood out of the water, gazed down arrogantly on the lord of morass. The enormous old alligator, cruel, cunning and powerful, commanded the bitter tribute of a fearful respect from the community of wild life in that vicinity.

The lonely morass was on Maybank Plantation, one of the vast rice estates of the Old South. For half a century the plantation had been deserted, and nature had long since completed her gracious work of covering the unhappy ruins of man. For a mile through the pine forest the black channel of the swamp wound a tortuous and sluggish course, arriving finally at a trickling, weed-choking outlet into the river. On each side of the narrow channel were water-lily beds, marsh tufts, clumps of buck cypresses and fringes of green and yellow duck oats. Beyond these was a growth of young cane, dense and rustling; and still beyond, the level brown floor of the pine woods swept gently upward and away.

There had been a time when the swamp had

The "First Flower of the Country," the Camellia

swarmed with alligators, when the great bulls had challenged one another from end to end of the dark channel, when the marsh beds held many an armored giant thawing out the chill of winter in the sweet summer sun. But those days, as the days of the plantation itself, had passed.

Some of the alligators had been killed by wandering hunters. During the heat and drought of long summers others had crawled off toward the river in search of fresher water and had never come back. One by one they had passed. Only the great bull, the most ancient and powerful of them all, remained.

His deep den under the wide-spreading roots of the osprey-haunted cypress held the source of a spring, so that his water supply was always fresh. His wariness kept him clear of the few lone hunters who occasionally penetrated those deserted wilds.

As the other alligators left, the problem of his own support became easy for the great alligator. He ruled the swamp, even to its most remote recesses, with a vicious, invincible power. He took heavy toll of the sportive trout that silvered like flashes of sunlight the dark water of the lagoon; of the gentle and beautiful wood ducks that built their nest on the hollow cypress limbs that brushed the water, trying to rear their fuzzy broods on the edges of the tyrant's kingdom; of the tall white egrets, graceful and mild; of the gaunt blue herons that stood in motionless, melancholy ambush, waiting for a chance to pierce a fish with their javelin beaks; of the wild hogs that rooted on the boggy shores; of the eager hunting dogs that swam the deep water; of all creatures that came to the haunted morass to drink.

But on this balmy July day, when the monarch viewed his rich domain with more than usual arrogance, moving with indolent strength and assurance among the broad lily pads, there floated to his nostrils a strange and fascinating odor, musky and penetrating. The nostrils widened until their black pits shone red; the cold, protruding eyes gleamed, and the huge body grew suddenly tense and eager. Determining the direction from which the scent came, the lone bull, almost without a ripple, sank from sight and rose a few seconds later forty yards nearer the shore. Here he lay under some sheltering grass, watching and waiting.

With soft-lunging strides a brown bear with her little cub, roguish and playful, came down the pine-scented, flower-bordered trail toward the lagoon. The old bear had never been this way before and she was wary, but the rich beauty and peace of the surrounding swamp, the gleam of water through the trees and the cool, delicious aroma of blueberries growing somewhere near made her forget her usual caution.

The cub, while not equally impressed by the promises of things material, was still equally unsuspicious and perfectly happy. Once or twice when the big bear grunted her affection to him he answered with a droll squeak of merriment and abandon. He imitated his mother's rolling gait. To him the whole world was a beautiful playhouse made especially for cubs.

Soon the mother came to a tall blueberry bush and, rearing up, drew down the drooping limbs laden with their misty-purple fruit. She crushed the sweet, succulent berries with grunts of satisfied desire.

The cub tried to follow his mother's example, but the first time he stood up he lost his balance and fell over backward, landing with much amazement but with no injury in a heavy tuft of grass. He rolled over on his side, too lazy for immediate exertion, and gazed with sleepy eyes at his mother who was stripping the last branch of its fragrant burden.

The cub swung his feet drowsily back and forth in the air, wondering mildly at his own dexterity.

Meanwhile the old bear, with a satisfied rumble, dropped down on all fours, turned ponderously about, looked at her baby with huge affection, nuzzled him about the sunny grass until he stood up, and then lunged on down the light-and-shade checkered pathway toward the shining water.

Passing a growth of slim cypresses they came to the rustling canebrake which fringes the lagoon. The old bear pushed her way through this until her head and shoulders were clear of the canes on the other side. Then she stopped, sniffed the air and listened. Close behind her, greatly excited because the tips of his furry feet were in the water, the cub wondered what this move might mean.

The morass was unknown to the mother, and for that reason she was apprehensive. But as she listened she heard nothing to justify her suspicions. The blue sky bent sweetly over them; the gray moss, pendent from every tree, waved silently in the aromatic breeze; two wood ducks of gorgeous plumage floated peacefully far out on the bosom of the channel. An amiable old bullfrog seated on a half-submerged mossy tussock eyed the bear with the air of a kindly patriarch. A gray sapsucker was following, upside down, the exciting promise of a dead cypress limb.

*Refuge for the Hunted, an Island in the Delta*

Still, the mother bear hesitated a long time before she waded into the morass. But some green alligator acorns and some silvery wampee leaves lured her clear of the canebrake. There she began to feed, and there finally she lay down on the quaking turf to wallow. The cub followed manfully, although he kept on a dry ridge of turf that extended out to the channel. He was about ten feet from his mother. Twenty feet away, with just his eyes and the point of his nose showing above the water, the Maybank bull marked his prey.

The lone alligator was intent on a kill. His glassy eyes gazed with unwinking speculation at his intended victim. He noted the old bear's apparent forgetfulness and the cub's separation from her. Just at that moment the little fellow was trying in vain to make a playmate of a stolid terrapin, half grown, that was trying to pretend he was really nothing at all.

Measuring the distance the alligator withdrew silently beneath the black waters. A moment later his eyes rose ever so gently out of the grass-grown lagoon not six feet from the innocent little bear, which was then slapping playfully at the gaudy dragonflies as they flirted past him. His mother, although watching him now, was still some distance away wallowing in the weedy water.

Stealthily, and under the ambush of the glistening wampee leaves, the bull drew closer. As he swam, he turned to give his mighty tail room to sweep the cub into his crushing jaws. Inch by inch he drew nearer, leaving but a tiny oily ripple in the water behind him.

There was a short rush, a lunge, the flashing whirl of a mighty tail—like some broad, black scimitar—a terrified squeal from the cub, a furious snort and plunge from the mother. The bull's tail had grazed the cub, tumbling him stunned into the water; the mother struggled wildly but vainly in the sucking mud; the red mouth of the great alligator, terrible with tusks, was already open to seize his victim lying only a foot away.

But then from the opposite bank of the lagoon there came the clear, sharp crack of a rifle, and a white tuft of smoke floating up from the canebrake.

In an instant the scene was vividly changed. The old bear worked free of the morass, reached the cub and stood defiantly over it, her great sides heaving in an agony of maternal fear. Almost within reach of her paw, turning in slow, blind, painful circles, with a heavy bullet in his brain, was the lone bull of Maybank—helpless, shattered, dying. His dark blood stained the stagnant waters that he had so long and so cruelly haunted.

Across the lagoon on a fallen log an old hunter watched this second scene; and even as he watched, the third and last scene was enacted before his eyes. He saw the cub, nuzzled by his fierce old mother, stir feebly; and then the great bear sat back on her haunches, took the cub in her huge, soft arms, rose on her hind legs and stalked growling out of the morass to disappear in the purple twilight of the pines.

The hunter could have shot her easily, but he let the old creature carry her baby away in safety. The bull alligator ceased moving, quivered, turned slowly over and lay still. And the hunter stepped down from the log and started for his far-off camp.

Over the great swamp there fell a silence, such a silence as it had not known in many years.

It was a silence that would never be broken by the hollow, terrible roar of the lone bull or the pitiful cries of his victims, but only by the melodious winds choiring through the mighty pines and the happy songs of birds.

# Plantation Dwellers

IT WAS a midsummer afternoon on the plantation.

"Lord bless us, Scipio!" my father cried heartily. "That cloud is coming pretty close. Call in the boys and tell them to come to the front piazza."

"'E will rain," the gaunt Negro responded. Then, putting his hands to his mouth he gave a long, melodious whoop in a voice that would have set jaded operagoers tingling. In immediate response to the summons a troop of laughing children came scampering out of the tobacco field and followed the Colonel and Scipio up to the Great House.

Merry, rolypoly, happy, scantily clad, they straggled up the broad cypress steps and gathered in a whispering group at one end of the wide piazza. The effect of the Great House on them was to make them wisely grave and urchinly solemn. Taking shelter on the porch of the Great House was a privilege and an honor.

Father, who had disappeared into the house, returned with a long blue china dish piled high with steaming hot sweet potatoes. He had had them cooked especially for his little workers and insisted on bringing them out himself. The children were shy at first, but when the understanding old Colonel had left them to themselves they very soon demolished the sweet potatoes.

The day had been a typical one for August in the Santee country. A cloudless morning had been followed by a succession of thunderstorms which left the earth and the air drenched with fragrance and refreshment. After the last rain there would come a cool and perfect late afternoon; and for its coming the Colonel, Scipio, the children and I waited on the piazza of the house that stood in patient majesty under the downpour.

The Great House stood in a semicircle of live

oaks—gigantic, moss-draped and dreamy with ancient age. Behind the house flowed the wide yellow Santee through the mighty rice field delta; before it the field of cotton, corn and tobacco stretched away to the pinewoods, whose pale purple crests were now misty in the rain.

But thunderstorms in August do not last long, and soon the clouds began to break and the rain slackened. The breast of the sea-going storm could be seen, a gray banner waving between the earth and sky, passing over the far rice fields beyond the river.

Then the sun came out in sudden blaze, and the long cotton rows in front of the house steamed in the heat. A cool wind, delicious and fragrant, came out of the great pine forest and stirred the dark rich foliage of the tall corn. The drizzle ceased abruptly, and the children, who had sat quietly enough during the storm, began to grow restless. They talked in whispers and leaned out far over the edge of the piazza to look up prophetically at the sweet blue patches in the pale, clearing sky; they chased one another with subdued delight in limited circles; they rolled and tumbled in the rough sandy holes where the concrete floor had disintegrated.

"Boys," called the Colonel—with little regard

*Oak by the River*

for particulars since most of them happened to be girls—"no more work today. Come up soon in the cool of the mornin' and finish clearin' out that corner. It's time to start home now."

They froze at the sound of my father's voice and then began to file slowly and with much dignity out of the piazza. When their bare feet touched the ground they seemed once more charged with their natural freedom and happiness. They sang and shouted and danced down the wide sandy road, happy in the thought of the day's work being over, happy in the thought of going home and of tomorrow's toil; or perchance just happy without thought, as children sometimes can be.

The Colonel and Scipio watched them disappear—some through the old gray gate leading into the pinewoods, some into the tall corn that waved fragrantly above them, some across a field overgrown with broom grass and scrub pines, beyond which lay the road to the next plantation.

The sun began to touch the pine tops, and its long level rays swept for miles over the mysterious landscape. The gray oaks, the deep corn, the great dim cypress swamp beyond the river and the misty rice fields were all bathed in orange.

My father sat down on the edge of a huge block of cypress, cut from a single tree and used as a pi-

*The Great House*

azza table, and Scipio settled on the floor against
the base of one of the porch pillars. The mournful sweet yowling of a hound briefly broke the
mellow silence of early evening. Its music and
spiritual quality harmonized completely with the
serenity of the plantation.

I love a hound because he appears to me a dog
of some spiritual significance. His sagacity begins
where that of most dogs ends. He has a perception
poignant and true. He has taught me much about
life. My obligation to him is that unpayable debt
that we owe to those who have given us an insight
into the meaning of existence, whose spiritual gen-
ius has led us to understand that life has about
it a great deal more magic and mystery than people with dismally literal minds would have us
believe.

A hound is the only dog I know which cannot
be said to bark; he sings. He is a music maker,
and if he is well bred he takes his art seriously.
I love to blow a hunting horn just to get the
hounds' lyric reaction to it: bass, alto, tenor, so-
prano—the mournful sweet yowling begins. Some
hounds take the matter of their music so reli-
giously that often even on a hot trail they will stop

to go through the performance. And what they render will be real music. I have seen an old, proud hound with a superb alto about which he was inordinately vain fall considerably behind a running pack just to pause and give tongue.

Sometimes a hound will do a good deal more singing than the occasion appears to call for. I once asked a Negro why it was that a hound just revels in yowling rapturously on even the slightest, and sometimes on no, provocation.

"When I go to church," the Negro said, "I sing. An' sometimes when I is workin' turpentine I sing and whoop. I do that to ease my soul. A hound, he'll ease his soul the same way."

Possibly the smartest thing I ever saw a hound do happened late one afternoon while I was in a small outbuilding in the plantation yard that we call "the Castle." It had been a big smokehouse, but we put windows in, built benches along its sides and transformed it into a place where Negroes who came to see us could wait comfortably.

I was waiting there for a Negro who had promised to give me the exact street address of a flock of thirty-four wild turkeys that rumor said he had seen. Beside me lay a black and tan hound pup of which I was very fond. He was drowsing con-

*Under the Front Porch of Hampton*

tentedly with his head toward the open door, and
I noticed that he roused himself several times to
look out. I shifted my seat so as to get his line
of vision. Full in the doorway, regally framed
by the sunset, stood a sagacious old hound named
Ringwood, a black beauty with great down-hang-
ing ears, heavy dewlaps and a grand, melancholy
face.

Old Ringwood would bear watching. He had
a way of going skylarking at night all by himself.
Sometimes, when there was no apparent reason
for him to feel guilty, he would give me casual
sidelong glances. Also I heard rumors that sheep
miles from the plantation had been slaughtered
by a monstrous black hound. I had no proof of
Ringwood's involvement in this sinister business,
but I was uneasy about it. Yet the dog was so
superb after deer, and his career had been so long
and splendid, that I hated to suspect him. About
one thing, however, I was determined: he should
not ruin the pup.

Dogs are laughably like people; one may go
straight, but two will jump the traces. I have often
noticed that when two dogs take a shine to each
other, frolic much together, execute little secret
expeditions, from a soul mateship, it is high time
to look for trouble.

I had noticed a decided intimacy springing up between Ringwood and the pup, and while I counted on the old dog to train the youngster legitimately I didn't want any special courses in sheep killing. The pup was just like a schoolboy—innocent and ready for fun.

I could tell that he wanted to join the old hound, and would have but for my admonishing him to lie still. Yet the thing went on. Ringwood kept coming to the door, invitation glowing in his eyes. Once he whined enticingly. At last I told him shortly to get out. Crestfallen and thoughtful, he turned away. Within a few minutes, however, he had come back and stalked into the little room. He stood by the fire, gazing into its depths. He did not lie down. Infected by his mood I began the same kind of silent gazing into the flames. I was roused from my reverie by a slight scuffle beside me. The two dogs were already halfway to the door.

Ringwood had the puppy by the scruff of the neck and was gently and guilefully dragging him off for a frolic. The big dog's demeanor was so clumsily surreptitious that I couldn't be angry, and his maneuver was so crafty that my admiration was greater than my annoyance. Ringwood had figured out the whole thing in that massive

head of his, and his way out of the difficulty was
certainly as clever as a man could have devised.
He wanted the pup; the pup wouldn't come.
What then remained but to wade right in and
steal the comrade for whom he was lonely? I went
out into the yard with them, the world aglow with
sunset, and there I let them have their fun together. But I saw to it that they did not get out of
my sight.

I recall with what delight I used to watch a
Negro named Henry Washington feed a pack of
a dozen ravenous hounds. He had a long cypress
board divided into spaces, one of which was ap-
portioned to each hound. Bringing out the pot
of steaming food, he would line up his famished
army and address them thus:

"How come you ain't find you' place, Music?
Ain't you know you have a place at table 'tween
Buck and Doe? Don' you cross that line, Check;
I don' care how hungry you is. Gambler, you
ain't goin' git a thing if you edge up on me. Bugle,
if I bat you with this spoon, you' jaw will ache
till New Year's Day."

During this admonitory address Henry would
be ladling the food onto the big board, a portion
for each dog. He had them trained so that until
the banquet was properly spread, not a dog would

begin, though certain lean, melancholy faces would loll forward languishingly.

Of all the dogs that I have even known, Sarsaparilla, an alleged hound, was the least promising in appearance. He was named back in those old days when patent medicines and soft drinks were first making their way into the remote hinterlands of the plantations and Negroes got a kick out of naming their dogs, their children, and their mules Neuralgia, Asthma, Sarsaparilla, Ambrosia, and Dandruff.

This beast, Sarsaparilla, had other faults besides his effervescing name—he had apparently no sense at all; he was too tall; his head had no particular shape; his gait was an absurd walk. He gave the impression of traveling on stilts. His color was a discord of mangy yellowish white. His facial expression was notably vacant.

Sarsaparilla was simply ludicrous. He just wouldn't do. So, for a long time, I thought. But there came a day when I was to learn a mighty lesson about not judging by appearances. I was to learn that courage, like wealth, is solely a matter of the heart. And it took a yellow dog to teach me.

One morning when I went down to the stable yard, I was greeted by a shrill complaining from the hogs that were penned in the ample enclosure. When I came up I found that they had a visitor, a rangy wild boar from the swamps, a shaggy hyena-like creature with gleaming tusks, alarming bristles and a most truculent mien. He had jumped a low panel in the fence, and by setting two rails there I could capture him. The thing was managed. But when I came to open the gate he charged me, mouth wide, bristles high, tail erect. I got the gate shut not a second too soon. He checked his speed, champed his great jaws at me sullenly and then turned back to torment the other dwellers in the yard.

Not wishing to shoot the boar, I decided to catch him with dogs. I therefore repaired to a nearby settlement where I gathered seven dogs and as many helpers, all of whom read between the lines of my story the glad tidings of bacon to be had for the catching. We had a motley pack: a bulldog, two hounds, an alleged collie, two plain curs of the most obscure antecedents and Sarsaparilla. I remonstrated with Sarsaparilla's owner about bringing this soft drink to the slaughter. He laughed in a shamefaced way, as if he thought his dog were being taken along to be the clown of the fray. I recalled the boar's size and mien, looked at this burlesque on rickety stilts, and pity filled my heart.

On reaching the barnyard, we decided that an assault *en masse* was the proper maneuver. The dogs were to be the shock troops, and we were to follow up the advantage that they would obtain over the enemy. We had sundry cudgels and ropes with which to belabor the victim.

The seven dogs went through the gate in a body, and the wild boar accommodated by rushing them. With great valor we watched the fray from the safe side of the fence. Suddenly, hurled high over the fence, the bulldog rejoined us; all the zest was gone out of him. Then the two hounds fled across the yard and skulked into the stable. The collie stood off and barked with hollow ferocity. The two plain dogs went manfully to work, as if the supply of bacon interested them personally. One dog was trampled by the boar and the other seized the monster's ear and hung on grimly. Yet the beast would rip him open, I knew.

Just then, Sarsaparilla, who had calmly and aloofly watched proceedings, stepped niftily in. He approached rather fastidiously, not from dismay but with a certain regard for finesse. Stationed behind the hog, he looked thoughtfully at the shaggy brute. Then he quietly bowed his lunatic, dolesome head, mouthed the boar's upper haunch until he had a deliberate hold, sank his teeth, set his legs and began grimly to shake his head.

The boar, I think, got one glimpse of what had him. He probably imagined it a saber-toothed tiger. Savagely shaking off the dog from his head he squealed shrilly and turned to run. Sarsaparilla said quite firmly, "Not so fast."

The bewildered boar could not get loose. The other dogs came back. We jumped the fence and soon we had the old marauder from the swamps securely roped. Sarsaparilla then stalked sedately off; he had condescended to help us, but he was not going to join in any of our puerile excitement.

"What kind of dog is that?" I asked his owner.

"God in heaven knows," he replied, "but he got *all* the sense. Sometime I goin' change his name to Solomon."

The character of the hound appears to undergo no change as the generations pass; he will be as he has been and as he is. His character has much to suggest to the human heart.

# AUTUMN

# A Nice Arrangement

THE WHOLE thing started the day Vincente Blasco's motorboat ran out of gas on the river opposite my plantation. "I thought something would happen to you on one of your pleasure jaunts someday, Vincente," I said as I met the little Italian on the big cypress-plantation wharf.

Beneath Vincente's piratic mustache his white teeth gleamed. He had an engaging smile. "I need de gas," he explained. "My tank, heem dry."

"Can't you burn moonshine?"

"Too much expense," Vincente explained seriously.

"I can let you have five gallons. Will you bring it back next week?"

"Yes, and bring you seex for your favor."

A sudden thought came to me. "Look here, Vincente, I want to show you something. While your man is getting the gas, just come over here with me by this big oak."

I led the Italian down a short stretch of river overarched with jasmine vines and dimmed by myrtles that exhaled fragrances as we brushed the bushes. We emerged on an open glade under a monster live oak—a vast tree that must have stood there for centuries. Over it clambered huge man-bodied vines; and growing on the marvelously long limbs, some of them parallel with the ground and not more than five feet from it, were fairy forests of vivid green ferns. Near the base of the oak I paused.

"Some tree," said Vincente, his quick black eyes appraising the majesty of the monarch.

"I didn't bring you here to look at a tree," I said. "You've seen plenty of big ones in Italy. But, Vincente, I want you to see what came my way yesterday. You're interested in natural history, aren't you?"

I stepped around the tree, pulling Blasco by the arm. Pausing, I pointed to something hung against the rugged bark. I expected an exclamation of awe from my visitor. All I got was a chirpy whistle of mild surprise.

"I killed it and brought it in," I explained. "There is a den out near a place called Jones' Pond. One was killed there two years ago. Now this one. And a third's been seen. I fastened this one up here this morning to photograph him. Seven feet, nine inches long, weighs twenty-two pounds, and has eighteen rattles. A diamondback rattlesnake, Vincente. You didn't leave anything like that in Italy."

"Ah," he breathed, as if he hadn't really heard me at all. And he stepped toward the snake and touched it with a delicate forefinger. "Ah, my friend," he went on, "eet ees a pity dat he is dead. If he was alive, I could make you an offer for heem."

"Offer?" I said. "What in the world would you do in the city with a monster like that? The whole police department would raid your fruit shop."

"A serpent like thees—deadly, terrible—he is what de people like to see. *Oh!*" he mimicked. "*Have you seen what Vincente Blasco has in hees shop on Broad Street? Eet ees one of de wonders of de world. It is a sea serpent. Eet ees a chimera. Eet frightened me, but I am glad I saw eet. So* they would talk," Vincente explained. "Dey would come. Dat means trade. I hear, too," he added, "dat rats have a fear of such a snake. I have too many rats. It would be nice arrangement."

"Perhaps I can get you one," I said. "What would he be worth? Mind you, I can't vouch for the niceness of the arrangement."

"I am no dealer in such pretties," Vincente answered. "But if he ees as large as dis one, and full of life, I give you feefty dollars."

"Next week," I answered, "when you come by here on the way to your still, leave those six gallons of gas for me and have fifty dollars handy."

It was the first week in October and I had little work on my hands. To ride the woods, to locate a big diamondback and capture him for Blasco— that seemed an easy and rather interesting way to make fifty dollars. Besides I would be ridding my own place of a creature that was a constant menace to man and stock. Only the month before, I had lost a Jersey heifer from snake bite. The thing was worth trying at any rate. And, anyway, I could take my gun along and scare up a covey or two. It was the first of the season and my setter Daisy was sick for a hunt.

Two days after Vincente's visit I made an early start for what I hoped would be a rendezvous with

a fine covey of quail and possibly with a diamondback as well. The pleasantness of the morning did
not seem in keeping with so curious and grim an
enterprise. An autumn haze hung over the river
and long lances of morning sunlight made the
mists sparkle. Sunbeams shattered against the purple tops of towering yellow pines and scattered
across the woods.

Mockingbirds warbled from smilax-crowned
hollies and cedars. Carolina wrens called to one
another with wild, sweet abandon. I heard one
quite near. And another answered from across
the river, a full half-mile away.

Daisy ran ahead of me, working the ground, full
of enthusiasm for the new and untried season.

The forest glimmered, and it was a radiant, dewy
morning into which I rode. The pine trash on
the road exhaled a spicy odor of freshness and wild
cleanliness. It did not seem the kind of world that
might hold peril and tragedy. It was a world made
for love and peace, for song and joy.

I knew where certain great diamondbacks had
their haunt. During the preceding summer my
neighbor Claude Marlowe, a woodsman of the
pineland, had killed one that was little short of
eight feet. I had wondered at that, and had examined it as it hung on a persimmon bush beside the

public road. And one of my hounds passing by it began to act curiously. He finally located the thing, backed away with the glint of ancient wisdom in his sagacious eyes and howled lugubriously before hurrying away.

Paris Green reported that he had seen, in the same locality, a snake of the same species and nearly the same proportions. Several other persons had had the dubious privilege of seeing one of these serpent wonders, and each had made his discovery in the neighborhood of Jones' Pond—a strange cypress-filled lagoon that lay on my place not two miles from the house.

I had tied a big burlap sack behind my saddle, and, stopping by a group of young hickories, I cut one that had a stout fork. I had caught snakes before. By pinning its head to the ground with the fork I would hold it tight until I could get my hand around its neck. Then I could lift it and thrust it down into the bag. I would leave my catch in the tied sack until I could return to the plantation for a wagon and a big box.

It may be thrilling, but it isn't exactly discreet to carry a diamondback in a flimsy bag. A mere scratch from an inch-long fang can do damage that no amount of wishing and sweating can repair.

Out of the plantation's far gateway and into the

lonely woods I rode. The bay branches drenched
in fragrant dew glistened and exhaled a winy fragrance. The sunshine filtered shyly into these remote solitudes.

I saw a buck, thin strips of velvet hanging in
tatters from his horns, slide into a myrtle thicket.
Woodpeckers were hammering in assiduous fashion, calling stridently whenever they paused in
their carpentering. Cicadas began to shrill, but
not so aridly as they would later in the day.

A half mile from the gate I turned off the road.
Far off in the open pinelands the lagoon appeared,
marked by its magical gleam of black waters, its
moss-hung bald cypresses, its aspect of perpetual
and mournful beauty. In those giant trees snowy
egrets nested, spectral in their loveliness like spirits of the place. In the dark waters alligators lived
their solitary, treacherous lives; and large-mouthed
bass of unbelievable size managed to exist by reason of their swiftness. Wood ducks nested in the
hollows of the cypresses and were often seen, as
placid and as beautiful as the waters themselves,
floating on that mirror surface.

To the right of the lagoon was a long savanna—
a green plain of many acres where flag flowers grew,
and gaudy flytraps and alluring orchis flowers. It
had an air of loveliness not quite familiar, not

A Quiet Cypress Pool

quite smiling. Toward this glimmering stretch of country I headed my horse.

It was the horse that gave me the first intimation that I had found what I was after. For a few yards I noticed that my animal—a little red pony that I enjoyed riding because of his sure-footedness in the woods—began to show a gingerly sort of stepping that I put down to his dislike of the lush, quaking surface of the savanna. I idly recalled that he had once spring-bogged down in a rice field, and I thought possibly that far recollection had returned to him.

Then he stopped. His head went up high. He trembled. His ears cocked. He gave a mighty snort as if he had scented some dreadful odor.

When he began to quiver violently I took it as a sign that we had both better be moving.

"It may be a snake," I considered. "Well," I added half aloud, "that's what I've come after."

I decided to dismount, but there were no trees near. A strange, scrubby, little live oak growing forlornly on the edge of a ridge of sand that crossed the savanna seemed the only place where I could tie my pony. That I must tie him was evident, for by now the animal was positive that his life depended on immediate departure.

I slipped from the saddle and led him firmly to

the oak bush, where I tied him fast. The morning was warm. I took off my coat and tied it to the saddle. Then I began to look about cautiously.

I whistled for Daisy and for the first time noticed she was standing. Could it be a covey of quail? Could it be an early-migrating woodcock? It might be a snake. As I watched how fidgety the dog was and saw the curious gleam in her eyes as she stared at the bushes ahead of her, I grew more certain that it was indeed a snake.

Down the ridge of sand I went, peering under the sparse growth of huckleberry bushes. Suddenly a curious odor assailed me. I knew it must be animal, but it seemed vegetable. It was like cucumber; yet its pungency was like bear scent. I knew what it was.

Under the bronzing huckleberry bushes lay the great serpent—larger than any I had tackled before. He had lately shed his skin, and in his tawny-gold phase he looked almost gaudy. Black and yellow and brown he gleamed on the white sand. He lay there indolently in a huge S-shape. He was certainly no plaything.

But after all, a man is a man, and a snake is a creation infinitely inferior. Against a sensible man even the hugest diamondback, lacking the advantage of surprise, is helpless.

I strode forward softly, my forked stick held before me. The snake seemed to bulge. His rattles began to sing their arid warning and he foreshortened himself. His bulk was amazing.

I had a curious feeling that I was intruding. Really, I thought, this is the diamondback's home, this lush savanna, this dreamy, stealthy place. The dim shores of this lonely lagoon were the serpent's by right of eminent domain.

Suddenly I remembered the dog. Jerking a chain from my pocket I walked around cautiously, fastened the snap to a ring in the setter's collar and led her away a safe distance, where I tied her to a thick bush. Daisy whined uneasily.

Returning, I found that the great serpent had not moved. I extended my forked stick, parting the bushes. A man must be sure that he is dealing with only one snake since these beauties often come in pairs.

Now the fork was close to the snake's massive head, and there was a good chance that the reptile would strike at it. I did not want to infuriate it more than necessary, though capture would assuredly madden it. With a deft maneuver, avoiding the spade-shaped head, I thrust the fork down strongly behind the massive jaws. The pointed ends of the stick buried themselves in the sand. The diamondback was securely caught.

As I expected, the body of the snake writhed

weirdly out of the bushes, rattles whirring wildly. The powerful muscular body contorted into fearsome coils, turned and twisted above the copper-colored huckleberry leaves. Keeping the fork tight, I approached. I had done this before, but something told me to beware. Several times in my life I had had what seemed premonitions. I certainly felt one now. But there was the promise to Vincente.

Stooping, with my stick held tighter than ever, I thrust my hand under the bushes and touched the snake's back. I slid my hand down the gorgeous broad hide until my fingers were just behind the fork. Then I closed them like a vise around the snake's throat. I tossed the stick into the savanna and tried to rise from my stooped position.

The effort made me momentarily careless, and I found myself suddenly struggling to hold my grip on the diamondback's neck. I slipped as I lifted that massive writhing weight. But I steadied myself. I was apparently master of the situation after all. I took a step toward my horse.

The red pony had witnessed the whole singular performance, and there was no denying that he understood everything—everything save what he believed his master's arrant folly. He stood quite ready, determined even, to make a bolt.

## A Nice Arrangement

The body of the diamondback writhed upward.
Before I realized what was happening the snake
had coiled its immense body around my left arm.
Partly because of pain, partly—certainly—because
of anger and wholly because it was struggling for
its freedom, the reptile began to constrict my arm.
At first I kept my eye on the pony and was not
really aware of what was happening. Other ser-
pents had done precisely the same thing before.

Walking slowly toward my pony, I spoke sooth-
ingly to it. Then I glanced down at my left hand,
which was extended away from me, and to my
horror I saw that the rattler's head was moving. It
seemed to have some new strength that I could
not control. At the same time, I felt a certain dim
but positive numbing of my left arm.

The diamondback was tightening his coil on
my bare arm in a grip that was deadening. It meant
that my hold on the snake's neck must inevitably
weaken. In fact, it was loosening already. I knew
it. The great serpent appeared to know it too, for
it continued slowly but remorselessly to tighten
its coil. It was like a wrestler who gets a purchase
on his antagonist.

Unless I could do something quickly the snake
would be bound to free his head and strike. I dared
not reach around with my right hand, for, not

knowing just what liberty the reptile had gained, I did not know whether it might not be able to launch itself forward for an inch or two, sufficiently far for a strike.

I thought of stooping down, laying the snake's head on the sand and trying to crush it with my heel. But such a maneuver with a serpent of this size and strength could too easily end in a fatal bungle.

There was the chance that I might hold my grip until I could ride to the plantation for help. It would take only a matter of a few minutes. That suddenly seemed the best way out—if I could hold on. But could I? I had encountered something too formidable for me. I felt myself outmaneuvered and overpowered.

Few people realize the strength of a large serpent. I began to realize it. The thing had me. I would have to get help.

But I had forgotten for the moment that the horse was fully aware of the nature of the thing I was carrying. As I approached, the red pony backed away snorting, straining at the buckhide thong that tied him. Even the stubborn live oak bent with his frantic pulling.

While I was still five yards away I saw that I would never ride home on that horse with that snake. There are some things that simply cannot be done. I doubted if I could get near the red pony, much less mount and ride away.

I paused, talking to him the while. A horse knows the tone of fear, and it fills him with apprehension. There was the red pony, his head and neck extended, the thong taut as a bowstring. There was I, a horrible thing in my hand, my arm banded by the cold coils—a tortured man trying to speak words of assurance. There was the diamondback about to slither out of my nerveless grasp.

There seemed no help. I thought of Vincente Blasco and cursed him in my heart.

I looked about desperately. The long sandy ridge spanning the pale green savanna offered nothing. The beauty of the bright woodland mocked me. Flocks of bluebirds filled the air with rivulets of song. The sunshine made the savanna twinkle with myriads of lustrous lights. There was a fragrant, meadowy scent of dew, of lush foliage and rare flowers in the air.

But this was irony. Here I was fighting for my life.

Then I saw something. The red pony was tied with a half hitch to the oak. The same kind of tie fastened the thong to the bridle. I needed that tough, pliable piece of buckskin. Whether I could get it or not was the question. Undoubtedly the pony was about to break away. Would the thong break, or would it pull off at the end? I had to have part of that thong. I stepped forward toward the horse.

The pony knew I was demented. He reared, plunged. I walked toward him holding my fettered left arm behind me, away from him. It drooped with exhaustion and with the dead weight of the diamondback. I was almost there. The pony blew out his breath in a long, amazed snort. He pawed and bickered. His eyes bulged large and showed white. His ears shot straight forward.

I pushed my right hand forward to get it on the dangling tip of the half hitch. The horse tried to bolt, but the thong held. He curveted until he almost ran around me. He bucked violently and tore loose.

The red pony was free; and he completely appreciated that freedom. He flashed through the edge of the savanna, snorting loudly, with stirrups flying and clanking, his head high, his mane and tail streaming.

My horse was gone; the buckhide thong was gone; my best chance for safety was gone.

But there was Daisy. Almost in despair I turned

toward the setter. Burdened by the ghastly rattler that was draining my strength, I staggered toward the faithful setter. She must understand.

With a spasm of renewed hope I tried to grip the serpent's neck more tightly. I came almost to where Daisy waited. I sank to one knee, extending toward her my imprisoned arm, almost powerless in the convoluted strictures.

"For God's sake, Daisy, help me, but don't let it get you," I said.

Daisy had all the delicacy of breeding of an English setter, and she knew the nature of the snake. But her master was in danger. What will not a dog attack for the sake of a beloved human being? If Daisy had cringed I would have been lost.

Suddenly she sank her teeth in the rattler's great bulging back. Feeling my arm more free I tightened my grip as the serpent released its. Daisy held on grimly. I reached down and untied her. Together we bore the monster to the waiting sack.

"Turn him loose now," I said. And Daisy did.

Into the burlap bag I dropped my burden. Then I tied the mouth of the sack shut and dragged it into the sultry shadow of the little oak. For a time I sat on the ground, exhausted. Daisy lay with her head in my lap.

I got to my feet, breathing heavily. In the high

pines near the lagoon, pines that now murmured and waved in an ecstasy of morning gladness, parula warblers chanted their elfin melodies. The sun gleamed and glinted across the savanna.

I thought bitterly that the same melodies would have sighed through the trees, the same sunlight lustrally gleamed, had the snake made an end of me. I had long since learned what every true woodsman knows: that under the beauteous garb of nature beats an indifferent heart—that to him who sees true, the countenance of nature has always about it something not quite intimate, not quite safe.

I caught the red pony on the borders of the lagoon. From there I retraced my steps to the rattler and carried it rather gingerly out toward the road, where I laid it in a heavy bed of gallberry bushes.

To ride back to the plantation and return with a wagon and a box for the captive was a matter of only a half hour. And in an hour I had the huge diamondback free of the sack and safely in a commodious box with a wire front. But I built a little extension and put in a second wire front to protect the first—or to protect those who were curious enough to investigate. The whole awful arrangement I put in an empty feed house, to await the coming of Vincente Blasco.

*Lock and Key on the Ballroom Door*

In a few days the familiar spluttering of the Italian's motorboat engine echoed on the river, and, true to his promise, he delivered my six gallons of gasoline. He found me somewhat grim and silent.

"How about da beeg snake?" he asked. "You cannot catch so easy, I know. Maybe next week, next month?"

"You can get him today," I replied in a most disinterested fashion.

"You got heem? Live? Beeg one?"

"Big enough," I admitted. Vincente drew out his wallet. "I have feefty for you," he said, peeling off the tens from an astonishing assortment.

"Now, Vincente," I said, "this thing you are getting is a dangerous thing. You understand?"

"I want heem dangerous," the little Italian answered.

"But no monkeying with him," I warned. "You must keep people away from him, and you must stay away yourself."

"He not much to handle," Vincente said easily. "You catch heem, do you not?"

"Yes, I caught him."

"Easy?"

"Oh, yes," I responded dryly. "I just lassoed him and dropped him in a sack."

Vincente, always a bit of an actor, suddenly made the deft motion of throwing a lariat, then of lifting something heavy that he had caught. "Like dat?" he queried, his white teeth flashing.

"Well, yes," I admitted grudgingly, "but with a good deal less effort."

"I will get heem now," the Italian said. "You ought to go into de business," he advised, his sharp black eyes gleaming. "Easy money."

"Thanks."

"You could catch many beeg snake. Dat leetle nice dog," added Vincente, eyeing Daisy. "You sell heem?"

"Not for a million dollars," I said, "and your moonshine business to boot."

"How about another nice little arrangement?" he asked, his black eyes yearning.

"No," I said, with a decision unusual for me. "Once is quite enough."

# The Kings of Curlew Island

THE ANTLER was massive. It measured not less
than five inches around the handsome beading,
and there were nine clear points, all genuine tines.
Architecturally the beam was perfect. Although
it was gray from weathering and had lost some of
its impressive weight, I had never seen a trophy
which interested me more. Wild woodland beauty
and romance, caught and made permanent, were
contained in such an object for me.

"Well," I asked, "and where did you find it,
Richard?"

"Cap'n," said the smiling Negro woodsman, "you already know."

"On Curlew Island?"

He nodded.

"This year?" I asked.

"I pick up this horn a month ago," he replied, "an' this same buck I done see no later than Wednesday, this same week Wednesday."

"And you mean to tell me, Richard, that he was wearing a top hat like this?" I questioned, eying first the tremendous antler and then the trapper.

"He order a larger size this season," he assured me, a smile creasing his face.

When it comes to sporting matters of this kind I am inclined to be abrupt. "When do we start?" I asked.

The suddenness of my question did not surprise Richard. He knew me too well. Almost from the cradle we had hunted deer together in the wilds of the Carolina coast country. He was very well aware that while the years may change the color of a hunter's hair, and perhaps the sprightliness of his step, they cannot touch the fiber of his heart.

"Today would be a good day to go, Cap'n," Richard suggested.

I appraised the westward-sloping November **sun.** Then I looked toward the lonely barrier

*Hunting Horn on Horn of the Hunted*

island five miles away across the lonely sea marshes
—beyond many a solitary bay and creek and sound.
To reach Curlew Island we would have to row
through winding creeks, which from the stormy
inlet north of the island spread octopus arms far
through the vast retiring marsh.

"Your boat—you have it here, Richard?"

He pointed toward the landing in front of my
house. "I didn' even tie her up," he answered,
" 'cause I knowed you'd go."

Four hours later Richard and I were on Curlew
Island. Darkness had fallen but it was a scented,
mild and starry darkness. It seemed that we had
come to a world of sea winds, sea stars and strange
lonely beauty. We were surrounded by the per-
fume of dew-drenched myrtle and oleander, the
sere rustling of the palmetto thickets, the mournful organ music of the mighty pines, the fluting of
a passing flock of yellowlegs. I heard the wings of
wild ducks winnowing the warm air. The roar of
the surf from the front beach sounded incessantly.
We had come to a strange, wild place, Richard and
I; and we had come for a romantic purpose.

We hauled our boat into the myrtle thicket and
then made our way down the dim trail, glimmering
now in the starlight, which led to the old cabin
that the Negro on his occasional trapping trips to

the island was accustomed to occupy. On either side of us were black thickets, full of perfumes, rustlings and the hush of listeners. Three times I distinctly heard deer bound away. You can't mistake the running of a deer—that light, incisive thudding of precise and trimly handled hoofs. Once I saw a tall flag tail stand out vividly white for a moment, and then suddenly vanish down a dark woodland aisle.

"I think, Cap'n, we might walk a little careful," Richard said casually.

"We are liable to fall over ourselves," I agreed, not understanding just what he meant.

"Not that," he corrected me, "but I mean you mustn't make no mistake and tramp on that big rattlesnake what done kill one of my dogs."

His calm warning nettled me. "Richard, what are you bringing me into—here in the dark? Why in the world didn't you tell me about this business before we left home? We shouldn't have come down here at night. I suppose," I added bitterly, "if the stag has eighteen points on his head, the diamondback probably has as many on his tail."

Like most men on a dark and lonely road, my attitude toward a rattlesnake is wholly conciliatory. I would just as soon let him have the broad highway to himself if he wants it.

"I done kill the mate," Richard told me.

"Large one?"

"My dogs ran into 'em by an ol' oak stump, Cap'n. I kill one snake, an' the one snake done kill my dog Poacher. The other snake git away under the stump. I lost one snake an' one dog."

"How long did Poacher live after he was struck?" I asked.

"He didn' live at all. Nothin' don' live after gettin' what he got. The snake strike at Scramble too, but Scramble make a sharp dodge."

"That's what I feel like doing now, Richard. Confound you! I suppose the island is full of these little friends of the hunter."

"Just them two," the Negro assured me.

I knew him well enough to trust his word on matters of woodcraft, but I persisted. "How long was your snake?"

"Bad luck to measure a rattlesnake, Cap'n. But if you had his rattles at a frolic you wouldn' need no jazz band. He's a swamp rattler—about eight foot long. But he was littler and tamer than the other'n."

"Real thoughtful of you, Richard, to save the big one for me—and me for the big one."

At that moment there appeared before us in the open space in the forest a squat and staggering building that I have dignified by calling a cabin. It stood in an arenalike place of sparse bushes and white sand. About it were huge oaks which seemed to meditate in the calm starlight. It was with real relief that I left the dark, haunted woods and entered this old clearing. There objects could at least be discerned on the pale sand—objects like an eight-foot diamondback, let us say.

But whatever resentment I had against Richard soon dissolved. He lighted a bright fire of dry driftwood and soon had the cabin cheerful. He prepared an excellent supper. Then there were smokes. All seemed well. Life was worth while despite reptiles and such. When I retired it was to dream of stags with treelike antlers parading before me, begging to be favored with a soft-nosed bullet from my .250-3000.

Next morning, before the dew was thinking of drying, I began my earnest stalk of the great buck of Curlew Island. We had not been out an hour before I had proof that this particular deer made his home on the island. I first struck the master stag's track in the black mud on the marshy edges of a fresh-water pond. It was a wonderful track, and the mud's consistency was so tough that I knew the track was not exaggerated.

"But this must be a calf," I said to Richard.

"Aren't there still some wild cattle on the island here?"

"Yes," he agreed, "but the track you see here is the track of the Curlew King."

"Sounds romantic," I said, " 'the Curlew King.' Well, we're here to do a bit of dethroning."

We followed the track. It led from the pond side into a marshy basin; thence it traversed a wild reedland crisscrossed with many animal paths. In this wilderness of reeds were hummocks of cedar underbedded with soft golden broom sedge—ideal drowsing places for deer.

And three times out of such shelters we jumped deer—two does and a sprightly buck bearing spikes. They rocked away in standard fashion. We were hardly interested in them. The track we were on belonged to an entirely different kind of creature. It led into the gross myrtle jungle between the reedy wasteland and the sea, where we seemed to lose the trail.

While each of us was wondering just what to do, and while the light and warmth of the morning sun sifted genially down on us through the piny boughs, both of us spotted something not thirty yards off, nestled in the most deerlike fashion on the brink of a vivid green savanna.

*Doe, Feeding*

Richard caught my arm and pointed with a steady finger.

Slowly I lifted my rifle. Then I lowered it. "Did you think it was the King?" I asked him in a whisper. Then with more assurance in my tone I said, "It's nothing but a cow. I can't see its head. But if I'm not mistaken, Richard, it's a dead cow."

Together we approached the prostrate creature. It was a heifer, dead. Her coat was so clean and beautiful and her condition so prime that I knew her death must have been a sudden one. I thought she might have tripped in a hole and broken her neck. Such accidents sometimes occur. But Richard discovered the truth.

"She fall," he said in answer to my guess, "but she was like Poacher. She was dead when she fall."

"A snake?"

"Not *a* snake, Capn', but *the* snake. They's just one snake can do a thing like that."

"I suppose so," I agreed, feeling creepy and beginning to eye the landscape with that singular alertness that awakens in a man when he senses he is in deadly peril.

"In the neck," Richard said, lifting the cow's lank head and pointing to a swelling at the place where the great artery comes from the heart.

*140*

"Come on, Richard," I said impatiently, "don't start that snake talk of yours. We are after a deer, not a diamondback."

"That so, Cap'n," the Negro agreed. "But if that cow couldn' smell him, and so done tramp on him, I might do the same thing. I ain't ready to tramp my last tramp yet. The Lord knows I ain't quite ready to sail on the Jasper Sea."

I had come to the island for pleasure and excitement, yet a sense of dread and distaste was coming over me. But I was determined to shake it off.

"We should have brought Scramble," I remarked, changing the subject.

"He's a good varmint dog," Richard said, "but he ain't so good on snakes—except in the dodging line."

"Snakes be hanged!" I exclaimed. "I'm thinking of deer."

We trudged down an old wood road that was densely flanked by a semitropical jungle. Richard had put me a little out of humor, and no man in a bad humor can do any decent stalking.

"Cap'n," said Richard after a while, "know what I think?"

"Well?" I queried, hinting by my tone a certain disrespect for any thoughts he might be having.

"I think," he said, "that Curlew Island ain't got just one king. There's the master buck and there's this same thing that keeps crossin' our trail."

"Well," I replied, "perhaps there are more than *two* kings on this island: You are the King of All Fools and you've made me the King of Uneasy Walkers. Do you know what I think, Richard?"

He admitted that I had the advantage of him.

"I'll tell you frankly, then. The trouble with us is we've almost in a funk. Every time I hear a jay-bird snap a twig I feel like breaking into a sprint. It takes real men to follow, stalk and bring down a stag like the one we're after. Do you think we're men enough to do it?

"Suppose you let up on this infernal snake talk of yours. I for one have the creeps and the jumps, and I know if I see a lizard I'll do a Brodie over these pine tops."

"All right, Cap'n," he agreed, not in the least out of humor. "But be careful."

"Hang it, Richard. Suppose you go back to the cabin. I'll try to trail this deer alone for a while. You take Scramble out and see what you two can find in the way of varmints. Then you can get a good dinner ready. Don't look for me till about dark."

"All right, Cap'n. . . . If you don't come back,"
he added with kindly, unconscious gruesomeness,
"I'll come to look for you."

"Thanks," I said shortly, "but I'll be able to get
home myself."

Little did I realize how much, before that day
was over, I should need the grim, good man I was
sending away.

With no further words we parted in the lonely
road. Richard returned to the cabin, and I struck
off at left angles into a dim trail through the fragrant woodland. I was in the wrong mood to cover
such country. I was too angry to be quiet, as a
stalker should be, or careful, which had been Richard's sound advice.

Yet this mood did not remain long with me. I
remembered why I had come to his wild island.
The vision of a stately crown of antlers once again
rose before me. Yet in such country stalking is not
easy. A hunter may pass within twenty feet of the
couched king, perhaps reposing in the brush, and
never see him.

Semitropical, languorous, baffling in its thickety
beauty, the virgin wildwood flanked my path.
There were tawny jungles of palmetto, the dense
greenery of cassina and of myrtle, beds of majestic

ferns. Overhead were moss-bannered oaks and old giant yellow pines murmuring musically.

On I walked through scented scenes that made me believe that in these woods the flowers never faded and the dew never dried. Yet they were silent woods. Few birds ever come to the island, except shore birds, which during migrations descend on it in countless thousands. Here and there I flushed a woodcock. Under almost every live oak I could see where wild turkeys had torn up the trash, and under the big pines they had raked the straw into long windrows.

Twice I started does from the thicket. One of these pushed itself gracefully through the myrtles, came to a halt in the dim road and stood for a moment gazing in startled fashion in my direction. She was just the sort of graceful, mysterious creature to inhabit woods like these.

But all this was not coming up with the King. It was now past noon, and November afternoons are short. From the forest trail I turned eastward toward the front beach. The deer of Curlew Island have always had the greatest liking for the sand dunes. A hundred yards from the beach, and while I was still in the woods, I came on a long, sandy slough. It was the kind of place where shore birds would delight to wade and feed, for it was

A Lagoon

Some White Ibis

marsh-margined and about half an inch under clear water. In the packed sand were scores of blurred trails. One of these that seemed very large, I followed.

Just as the trail entered the forest to seaward of the savanna I found one clear impression. There could be no doubt of it; it was the track of the King. And it was not an old track. A piece of damp sand displaced by the heavy tread of the giant deer still hung to the top edge of the impression. The track looked so hot that I knew if I had been a hound I would have begun to trail.

I examined the ground further. I came to a wide bayou, the consistency of chocolate. Here again was a track—wide, deep and almost straight, with tiny cuts and creases in it which could have been made only by a reptile's scales. Judging from the width and depth of the track my cold-blooded friend had a body not less than a foot in circumference.

Apparently I was on the trail of both kings. One I was eager to see; the other I loathed and dreaded. I made up my mind not to be diverted from following the stag. A curious stalk this was—trying to come up on one creature and at the same time avoid another. I was, in a sense, both a follower and a fugitive.

Cautiously I stepped forward, stooping under dense tangles, edging through titi thickets and trying to be as noiseless as possible. Quite near me I heard a wild turkey run. A gray squirrel must have seen the turkey, for he coughed a bark.

I was still on the track of the stag. I had managed to follow it, even in this jungle, because the earth was soft and almost clear of grass. But the work was slow, for sometimes the shadows hid the trail.

Northward turned the stag, and northward I followed. For two full hours I held the baffling, winding trail; then it headed for the beach.

The sun was down when I came to thinning trees and felt the breath of the sea wind. Then I saw the dunes, topped by their waving tufts of gray beach grass, and beyond them, in foamy tumult, the ocean.

Keeping the lee of a bulky storm-scarred red cedar, I came up quietly under its shelter. From this position I looked carefully up and down the beach. It was the very time of afternoon for deer to visit the sands. The rolling high dunes shortened the range of my vision, so I laid my rifle on the sands and pulled myself up into the first limbs of the cedar. To the southward the beach was bare—unless, nearly a mile away, the shadowy objects which I saw might be a troop of deer. I turned northward.

At first I did not see the stag. He was between two huge dunes, and he must have been holding his head down. But then he walked boldly, majestically forward, mounting a bare sand hill. Before my very eyes, and all unconscious of his peril, stood the King of Curlew Island. He was more than a hundred yards away—larger than life in clear relief against the sunset line. He was within range, but my rifle lay on the sands under the tree.

"Richard didn't lie," I said to myself as I eased my weight carefully down the tree. "That's the greatest buck on this island—*in this country*. His body isn't that of a giant—but his horns! I've seen antlers in my time, but not kingly crowns and chairs-of-state and all that."

For a shot at the great stag I had to do one of two things: either reclimb the tree—which was mighty awkward business with a loaded rifle—or re-enter the woods, pass down parallel to the beach for thirty yards or more, so as to get clear of the sheltering dunes, and then take a close shot from the forest edge. I decided on the latter course.

Sinking into the dark cedar grove I made my way as silently as possible through the borders of the dusky, fragrant woods. The twilight was fading. Momentarily I expected to be able to make my little maneuver toward the beach, but darkness was coming. Rather than lose precious minutes dodging in and out, I bided my time. At last, however, I turned beachward. And simultaneously with my turn I heard the diamondback! The thing seemed to be under my feet!

Insistent, shrill, querulously warning, the rattles whirred. The sound seemed everywhere. I was afraid to move. Always difficult to locate, this perilous note of menace was hopelessly so on the borders of the thicket. There was no light save a dim jungle glow, eerie and misleading. Moreover, I suspected this was the snake I had been avoiding. None other could probably sound its warning so formidably. I was so close that I thought I smelled the snake. I could not locate him, could not see him.

Right now my business was not to kill a buck, but to keep from getting killed. A single move in the wrong direction might be my last one.

Suddenly I heard the patter of running feet. Then there came a dog's sharp yelp. And out of the darkness behind me I heard a human voice call. It seemed to me to come out of another world.

"Oh, Cap'n!" shouted Richard cheerfully. The voice called me back from the realm of terror to

reality. It brought me to myself. I forced myself
to try to locate the snake. I heard the dog. He was
baying the reptile. They were between me and
the beach. I stepped backward into the thicket.
A few moments later I had joined Richard on the
dim woodland road.

"I thought you might need me," he said almost
apologetically.

"Is that Scramble back there in the thicket?" I
asked.

"Yes, Cap'n. What he been bayin' near you? I
don' hear him no more."

"He probably saved my life," I said. Then I
told Richard about seeing the stag and hearing
the snake.

"Scramble good at a sharp dodge," he said, "but
I don' know how well he can dodge in the dark."
Here Richard gave a long whistle, but there was
no response.

"You came just in time, Richard," I said.

And what of the buck? We left him for the
night. It was now too dark to shoot, even on the
dunes. But in my mind I could still see that magnificent creature gazing out over the somber twilight sea. Almost a phantom buck he was—a romantic shape of the rolling, ghostly dunes, a com-

rade of the wild sea waves, the mysterious marshes, the lonely forest.

"One thing good about this cabin," said Richard as we made our way up to the staggering structure which bulked in the faint starlight.

"So?" I asked disinterestedly, for its virtues had not impressed me.

"No rats," said the emotionless trapper. "A rattlesnake like to stay around an ol' place like this an' catch the rats."

"Cheerful little thought," I commented. "And, Richard, if you have any more of those happy snake ideas, suppose you give all of them to me in one spoonful. I don't care for the broken doses."

As we entered the cabin I felt uneasy, but Richard's blue-flame driftwood fire and his good dinner relaxed all my tension.

"Tomorrow," I said to him, "is the day. By the way, I hope Scramble gets back safely."

Richard laughed without feeling. "Scramble, if you could see him now, would look like an accident that is already happen."

"A daylight start," I said, "and tomorrow will be our last day on the island."

Dawn, with its aromatic sea winds and its blazing eastern star, found us once more abroad in the

*151*

island woods. Silently Richard trudged beside me. He was grieving, I knew, over the loss of his second dog. Within half an hour we were near the scene of our encounter of the evening before. Here the island begins to narrow to its northernmost point. The end of it, jutting out into a tawny inlet, was not more than half a mile from where we emerged from the woods onto the gray dunes. We mounted a high sand hill.

"It was off yonder that I saw him," I said, pointing to a group of dunes down the beach.

It was not yet sunrise. Sea mist hung over ocean and beach and forest, yet beneath its filmy canopy we could see far. The twilight of the morning shed its soft luster over the lonely ocean, the solitary sands, the silent fragrant woods.

"But, Cap'n," said Richard, with more excitement than I had ever known him to show, "ain't that the King down yonder?"

My fascinated eyes followed his pointing finger. Far down the northern end of the beach I saw a shadowy form. There could be no doubt of it. We were looking at the stag of Curlew Island. What I had last night left here on the sands was, after a long night's wandering, back again. Perhaps he was taking a last look at the ocean before retiring into the forest for the day.

"Cap'n, I'm thinkin' that he can't get away from us today." Richard's voice was quiet and assured. "He's at the narrow end and he'll have to pass us to get back to the woods."

"We've cornered the King, Richard. But look. He's going up the beach. He's going into the woods."

The splendid stag faded into the margins of the misty forest.

"That's all right," said Richard, "he's goin' to Eagle Pond to drink before he lies down. Come, Cap'n. I know the way."

No more perfect screen for a stalk could be imagined than was afforded us by the dense undergrowth through which we now, by winding animal paths, made our hurried and silent way. Richard led me to a big palmetto whose broad fronds spread fanlike to the ground. Crouched behind this perfect screen we looked out over the broad savanna before us. The place was about three acres in extent—a reedy clearing in the forest. Here and there were spaces of damp sand. Near the center of the savanna was Eagle Pond—dark and deep and just now fairly alive with mallards and teal.

"He'll have to cross this place," Richard told me.

I am not familiar with the kind of buck that has to do as a hunter thinks he should, but I felt this deer would walk out into the savanna. It practically spanned the woods here. Moreover, it must have been a singularly attractive place for him.

Silence and stealing morning sunshine and the sweet music of wild ducks' wings attended our watch. A lordly eagle beat his way powerfully over the amphitheater. I heard a wild hen turkey give her plaintive call. The surf fell sleepily on the drowsy shore. I was crouched low, my rifle thrust forward. I had everything in my favor for the shot of a lifetime—everything except the target itself.

Suddenly, silently, out of the mysterious forest he appeared. I measured the antlers with my eyes. Craggy, chstnut-colored they were—massive, symmetrical and with long tines. I knew he must be an eighteen- or twenty-pointer. And the spread of the beams was phenomenal; it could not have been under twenty-six inches. What a head!

A hundred yards away the myrtles had parted, and now he came forth clear.

"Shoot, Cap'n!"

It was the voice of Richard, and because of my hesitancy he came as near groaning in spirit as he will ever come.

I lifted my rifle to take the bead. The buck lowered his great head. His head came partly up, and I could see the bulge in his neck. Even at this distance I thought I could detect a defiance, a challenge in his aspect. Suddenly he whirled toward us, and for twenty paces he came head-on. Distinctly I heard him snort—the strange, whistling snort of a buck's defiance. He charged down the stretch of open sand toward us.

I was amazed, for I saw no enemy. It could not be that he was charging us. A wild buck doesn't charge a man when he can do anything else. I had my rifle on him. But my finger did not touch the trigger. The buck's behavior compelled me to watch him. I stood up. On the white sand in front of the stag was the object. This was the King's antagonist.

Parting the palmetto fronds with a cautious hand I saw the two fighters distinctly—the huge buck with his hair ruffled angrily forward, and the monstrous diamondback heaped in his coil.

The stag backed away, his grand head lowered and lolling with fury. He halted on the wet rim of the sand. I saw the reptile bulge himself, rising in his massive coils. I saw the spade-shaped head drawn back for the mighty drive. Then the buck charged.

When he was within ten feet of his enemy he leaped into the air, drawing his four feet together into a close-bound sheaf of incisive spears. With deadly precision he dropped on the snake; and as quickly as he had struck, he cleared himself. In another moment he had whirled and repeated his savage maneuver.

We watched fascinated. We were there to kill the buck, but I could not shoot him. Suddenly he halted, head held high, the picture of angry triumph. He had trampled the serpent to death. I saw dark blood running out on the white sand. The fight was over.

"Richard," I whispered, "you aren't saying 'shoot!' any more."

"He done make that snake pay up for killin' Poacher and Scramble," he replied, frank admiration in his tone.

"Well," I said, "a hunter may on occasion be a killer, but he must first be a gentleman. Look what that stag did for us. We've no right to kill him."

"He's surely the King," said the Negro.

"Yes," I agreed, "and because of what he's done for us, we are going to let him reign."

"An' to think, Cap'n," said Richard with a smile, as we turned away from the strange ending of our memorable stalk, "I don't even have to tell you no more to be careful how you walk."

# WINTER

# The Swamp in Spate

"A GREAT WATER, she's goin' to roll."

Such was the oracular announcement of Prince, my Negro boatman. We stood together in a balmy January sunrise on the long, lonely rice-field bank. He did not tritely say that there would be a freshet; he prophesied the rolling of great waters.

We are nine miles from the sea and feel the full effect of the salt tides which back up the freshet waters. Since the boundaries of the river country are narrower here than they are lower down, we get the dubious benefits of the flood's full height, over twenty feet.

In our region of the river country one of these spates rises for four or five days, remains almost stationary for a day or two and then slowly recedes. The length of its stay and the height to which it rises depend on both the winds and on the tides; an east wind backs up the water, as does a spring tide such as the full moon brings. Of course these forces determine only in part a freshet's height. Because of its pent-up momentum, and because of the vast suction of the sea tides, the fall of the water is more rapid than its rise.

The sea is an insatiable thing. I have stood on the beach on Cedar Island, which is at the tip of the delta, and watched the ocean gulp the ramping affluence of the tawny tide. Into the blue immensity of the Atlantic the river rushes, and the great sea absorbs it miraculously. But the sight of a freshet at the river's mouth is not nearly so impressive as one in the swamp.

Some twelve or fourteen miles above its mouth the Santee divides into north and south branches. By the time these reach the ocean they are a mile apart. Between them is the great delta—a vast, inchoate country, with her a gloomy moldering swamp, there a shimmering reedy expanse, here a warm winding creek teeming with wild life, there brakes of swamp blackberries and canes so dense that little more than the swamp rabbit and cotton-mouth moccasin can insinuate their way.

The north end of the delta is almost wholly a swamp—a swamp that affords at every step an exciting promise of something to be discovered, exciting fulfillment of some strange hope. Here abide the allure of mystery, the inviolate and forbidding depths. The swamp is a mystic, the keeper of some tremendous secret. Only when the river is in flood is one afforded some glimpses of it. Prince and I knew this; for many years we had seldom missed the opportunity to explore at such times the mysteries of that shrouded domain.

"Day after tomorrow the water will be getting near its height," I told him. "We'll leave early and come back late. You get the boat ready. I'll attend to everything else."

So, before sunrise on the second day following we were ready to push away from the plantation shore. The wharf at the river landing had long ago been submerged. The strange yellow tide lapped against the shore. Down the pathway on the bank, now under an inch of water, clapper rails, Wilson snipe, swamp rabbits, woodcock, and other refugees had gathered. Their presence made me think of Burke's "Public calamity is a mighty leveler." Along the wild fringes of the river, marshes and margins of duck oaks were drowned, and the alders, the shorter canebrakes, and all the bush growths were fast being submerged. The taller trees stood out like solitary lighthouses. The sun of the warm midwinter day was rising. Behind me in the safe dry thickets, towhees and parula warblers sang, but the peace of the calm day was belied by the angry aspect of the surging flood.

Having measured with a thoughtful eye the dimensions and the temper of the spate, I was not impressed with the quality of the transportation that Prince had provided for our visit to the swamp. It was a dugout. But the man who made it started wrong; he chose a cypress log too small for the purpose. Such an error is, to say the least, fundamental.

Our canoe had length and a certain tippy grace, but it was too wasp-waisted for its full length. As it lay against the bank, aspiring little waves leaped freakishly over its thin sides.

"Prince," I protested, "this is the best boat to get drowned in, or from, that I ever saw."

"When old Eli made her," he answered, "he said he might use her for his coffin."

But when we were once steadily seated in our frail little craft, she rode jauntily forth on the Santee.

## The Swamp in Spate

A freshet has more volume and vehemence than any other tide I know. It has a lawless exuberance, a spendthrift vigor. A flood is a triumph of incontinence.

As the home shores receded, the immensity of the flood widened before us. Far up the glimmering river I spied a tall rack of chestnut-colored antlers. There was a gallant buck swimming for his life out of the lonely swamp. He had probably come several miles, but the mainland was now in sight. A deer is a tireless swimmer, but I have seen more than one labor pitifully in the spate's mighty currents.

The very first refugee we saw repaid us for crossing the dangerous river. This fugitive from the flood was a full-blooded wild razorback—all bone and bristles and lean bacon. Her snout was so long and sharp that it gave her the appearance of smoking a pipe. Her sides were plainly slatted. Her ensemble was, for all her uncouthness, indescribably fierce. Her startling fringe of bristles was a sort of menacing triumph. Formidable indeed she looked—morose and vindictive—standing gingerly there on a sodden log, wedged precariously by the freshet tide into the low crotch of a water oak.

Brush and sedge, and the tree's limbs, had made

a tremendous islet that swayed in the rushing waters. Behind her, under her, quaking in the shelter of her flanks, were her little ones—nine of them. She could easily save herself, but she would not leave them to perish.

Knowing that the old mother could swim miles to safety I made up my mind to save at least some of the pigs. They were only about two or three weeks old, and in their present situation they looked to me doomed.

The waters were fast rising. The old savage creature knew well that she and her trembling brood must soon be dislodged from their frail support. About a half-mile away, across a clear stretch of water, there was some high ground known as the Pine Ridge. I watched her appraise the risk involved in reaching it. She had, I knew, determined to swim to the Ridge. But she wasn't going alone. Lowering her hideous, formidable head, she tenderly nuzzled the pigs, one by one. She grunted deep and placid reassurance to them. She kept nudging them until they were all in a huddle.

Then suddenly she plunged off the log into the stormy tide. She swam about thirty feet—fiercely and with head high, as a hog always swims. Then she headed around and in a few moments had returned to the log. She climbed it, streaming. As surely as I was watching her I believe that she was instructing her babies as to how the thing was to be done. And she was showing them how easy it was. Again she took gentle counsel with her nursery.

Slowly, with infinite caution and patience, she herded them down toward the water. She was actually in it, among the stranded sedges, for a moment or two, before she was satisfied that all her brood were with her. Then, grunting easily, very slowly she began to swim. All her tiny pigs were in the lee of her great flank. Seeing to it that they started on that side, she broke the current for them, and they swam as if they were in a backwater.

An hour later Prince and I found our gallant old sea-going heroine on the Pine Ridge. She had every little pig safely with her. I looked at the gaunt, grim creature with genuine admiration.

We next reached a hushed hiatus—a backwater full of eddies and of trash, to windward of a line of trees, to leeward of a vast canebrake. The tan-and-green tops of the canes whispered and hissed and rustled as the tide worked nervously with the submerged stems. Against the brake was a deep and long raft of sedge. On it nine swamp rabbits squatted piteously. Knowing little of man, they had small fear of him; and in a flood, fear of man in all wild creatures is somewhat abated, tempered by the apparently graver and more immediate menace of the rising waters. More than once when those timid little fur balls of the marsh have come in freshet time to the mainland shore I have caught them with no particular effort. When caught, they cry pathetically. One of the standard sounds of this weird delta country is the shrill wail of the rabbit. He has many enemies—owls, hawks, eagles, foxes, wildcats, to mention but a few.

We pushed our way gingerly through the tree trunks that marked the line of the lost riverbank. Here the tide hurried faster—eager, insistent, gulping trash, whirling in soft golden eddies. Though the freshet was at its height, and stopped as far as farther rise was concerned, the movement of the waters continued. We came to an ancient cypress, a pagodalike tree solemnly squatting in the water. Against its somber shelter we hove to, and I stretched out my hand to grasp a low-sweeping limb. A warning cry from Prince checked me. Numbed and distorted by cold, grimly savage over their plight, three huge cottonmouth moccasins lay huddled against the bare matting of boughs that moved sighingly in the current. They were monstrous old brigands from the vast delta country, mud-smeared, dully furious at having been washed from their hibernating quarters by the unsparing flood. I noticed that although their bodies were dirty and unkempt their heads were clean.

"Prince," I said, "they look cold. Will they strike?"

Prince is a good deal of an authority on snakes; he is the only man I know who has twice been struck by the cottonmouth and has lived.

"Strike?" he repeated incredulously. "Strike is the first thing and the last thing they do."

To test his words I presented a paddle, none too gently, to one of these drowsing monsters.

Swifter than the eye could follow he had struck the soft, water-soaked end of the cypress blade.

"What will become of them, Prince?" I asked.

"As soon as the water falls, some will crawl into bed again, but some will get washed away."

It is a fact that many of these river reptiles are carried on trash and logs out to sea, and that the sea islands near the river mouth are as a consequence badly infested by them.

From the haunted cypress we passed to a more pleasant scene. Northward from our canebrake a wide waste delta field had been submerged, but in one place a prodigious growth of reeds managed still to rise above the waters. There must

The Cardinal, Bird of Beauty, Known from New York
to Venezuela

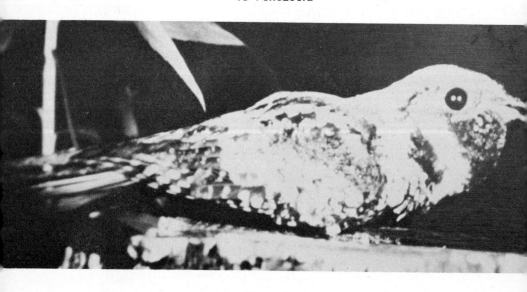

A Whippoorwill

have been five acres of nodding plumes, and from the sanctuary thus afforded there came the pleasant gossip of wild ducks. I knew from their voices that they were black ducks. As a rule, species keep together. Once I heard an old Negro say that mallards had "taken a contract" for a certain preserve; and it is true that the various kinds keep segregated, especially as the winter gives hints of waning. In the South the winter is continually doing that.

These black ducks were greatly enjoying their sunny retreat. The waters had obliterated their normal feeding grounds far down the river. At such times I have seen countless thousands of wild fowl thronging northward to find temporary new feeding grounds. When flooded out of the delta they repair to the salt-marsh creeks to the southward and to the great swamp to the northward, where abundant food always awaits them. Into the sere reeds of the sanctuary our lissome canoe insinuated itself, parting the frail obstructions like a water snake. As soon as we touched the sedges five ducks jumped up.

"The watchmen," said Prince.

Their cries startled others; then the flock rose. I roughly estimated the number to be five or six hundred. All these ducks jumped in precisely the same manner. A dash downward of the wide-webbed feet, a smart striking of the wings (often on the water), and the duck would bound upward to a height of about five feet. The bird would look awkward and tail-heavy, feet untucked, neck bent and craned. Swiftly they righted themselves, recovered their poise and gathered graceful momentum.

Emerging from the reeds we saw what we took to be a black log drifting. As valuable timber is always to be had in a freshet, we pushed toward it. Crossties drifting seaward are easily caught and tied up with grapevines until the water subsides. But a spate is full of surprises. We came within a few yards of our log and discovered an alligator instead, roused from his long sleep by the wintry flood. He was not swimming, but drifting swiftly and smoothly, his head and a little of his back showing. This nine-foot creature glared at us with wide-open eyes. Against such brutal treatment as he was suffering he seemed to be protesting to the gods in savage silence.

This bull was one of the few I have ever seen abroad in winter, and his presence was compelled. Knowing him to be merciless, I had it in mind to shoot him, but he appeared a momentarily helpless sort of dragon. We let Dagon sail glumly on.

How far would he go? Probably he would lodge against some tree or brake, and there wait shiveringly until the subsiding of the waters. Possibly he might drift out to sea, thence to be washed back on one of the coastal islands. I have a friend who is a gamekeeper on one of those barrier islands and he has told me that one day when he went down to the beach to bathe he found a huge bull alligator serenely riding the breakers. An alligator apparently passes without harm from fresh to salt water, and I have known many to live in brackish creeks.

We struck northward toward the fastness of the gray river swamp, mysterious and moldering, moss-hung, solitary, beauteous, forbidding. On our way we passed many refugees. Of these the rails took care of themselves best. Perhaps they enjoy a freshet. They travel along sedge heaps, busily probing; they fly across strips of water to patches of bushes; they forage along old drifted logs and dodge in and out of the sighing tops of the drowning brakes. On one small sedge strip I counted seven of these handsome birds. Four others picked their way gingerly through the heads of a suffocating reed bed. Their activity and apparent aplomb amid wide disaster were in curious contrast to the huddled misery of the rabbits.

*An Egret*

Nothing could be more forlorn than a tremulous bunny, soaked from a long swim, hunched disconsolately on the top of a stump, only too well aware that he is dangerously spectacular. Some of these swamp rabbits had climbed two or three feet high in vine-covered bushes. While the birds seemed to be enjoying the adventure, the rabbits, saturated with self-pity, timorous and palpitant, awaited their doom.

And now Prince and I entered the fringes of the swamp. A silence, vast, alien and portentous, brooded here. Here one was instantly aware of the ephemeral nature of human life, for here were giant cypresses that had been standing two hundred years. Man-bodied vines, the great muscadines, wreathed the cypresses fantastically. Here were giant pines towering ninety feet to the first limb. Out of their fragrant crests a faint music breathed. Tall tupelos there were, and stately gums, with here and there a holly or a red cedar rising sixty feet above the water.

I have never seen such hollies as those that grow in the swamp. They assume the cone shape of the hemlock, and when gaudily illumined with berries they look like Christmas trees for Titans. This part of the swamp, as yet untouched by man's hand, has the hush and the inviolateness of some fairy domain.

Our canoe moved easily through the flooded naves of the dim swamp. In this strange land, as in some mighty edifice, though the total effect might be gloomy, there were bright details.

Over the tolerant bulk of a cypress base a wild jasmine disported its clambering grace. Its evergreen vine festooned the gray base of the giant tree, lowering a tapestry starred with golden bells. Over many of the smaller trees hung mighty wreaths of smilax—verdant ropes fifty and sixty feet long, ending in a vast wreath completely crowning the victims of these effusive attentions. Here, too, were the scarlet berries of the swamp brier, the misty purple clusters of the sweet gum, the pale, cold mystic berries of the mistletoe. On many trees hung bunches of this gorgeous parasite large enough to fill a two-bushel measure.

On all these berries robins and cedar waxwings were feasting. Thousands of robins would be in sight at one time, a gay, roistering, caroling crowd. Little cared they for a freshet. The stern, sweet business of homemaking was far behind them and far ahead; now they were disporting themselves while spending the winter in the South.

Strange are the bed fellows made by a flood. As

we drew near a ridge I observed many forms moving on it. Drawing in close we came on a motley crowd, reminding me of the old pictures showing refugees from the Deluge. Literally they came down to the water's brink to meet us. There were some half-wild goats, but all their wildness had deserted them. They headed straight for the canoe, determined to board it. Always in floodtime certain animals recognize man as possible rescuers, or understand the safety that is supposed to abide in boats, or else feel a violent need of change.

After the goats came the hogs—bristling, long-snouted, snuffing creatures, wild marauders from the swamp's gaunt heart. Yet all things considered, and despite much general opprobrium heaped on swine, hogs are among the most interesting refugees from a flood. They are valiant swimmers, fearless to the point of truculence, at all times self-sufficient and resolute. They make short work of any rattlers or moccasins—or of anything defense-less. Roaming restlessly up and down this lone islet in a waste of spate, they are never disconsolate or timid.

If food becomes scarce, goats and sheep will stay and starve; of his own volition, a hog will plunge into the flood, and for miles sturdily breast a tide from which many a dauntless swimmer would shrink. They are grim and fierce and some have ancient notches and slits in their ears, testifying to the fact that man once had a claim to them; but hogs on the ridge are common property. Prince eyed them with especial interest. From the ridge to Prince's little strip of land abutting the river the distance is two miles. Often after a freshet Prince has welcomed strangers from the swamp to his home.

As we moved toward the north end of the ridge, five great forms launched themselves upward. The sun glistened on their bronzed backs. They were wild turkeys taking flight, beating their way off through the cypresses. In a freshet these great birds generally take good care of themselves. Often they come to the mainland; sometimes they stay in the trees of the swamp, foraging assiduously. Occasionally young birds caught in a region where food is scarce, and unaware of the abundance of it elsewhere, become greatly emaciated, but I never knew one to die of starvation. A flood in this part of the country never stays more than a fortnight, and a wild turkey appears capable of enduring a fast of that length.

It is not widely known, but a wild turkey can swim well. When I see one in flood water, however, I know that it is in a bad way. The tide, wet-

ting and chilling the bird, saps its strength. A turkey will seldom deliberately take to the water; but
sometimes it will begin to swim when the rising
tide covers its footing. Because of its more deft and
artistic poise, the hen seems a better swimmer
than the gobbler.

We came to a field of small cypresses growing so
close that I took hold of them on either side of the
boat to help Prince get the craft through. Swimmers in the freshet tide had been in sight since we
left home, but in this swamp thicket we were to
see our most interesting refugees. Almost black
he looked, incredibly lithe, gliding rather than
swimming, sinuous, swift, radiating a certain wild
intelligence. It was a big male otter—hardly, indeed, a refugee, for he was in his element. He was
in sight one moment only. Then he humped his
glossy back, rose abruptly on his glistening stom-
ach, took a header and was gone. We sat motionless
for five minutes, hoping that he would reappear,
but we saw him no more. During my roamings of
the Santee Delta and its environs I have not seen
many others, but they are there.

Now we came to a great lane in the swamp, an
apparently endless highway that Prince told me
had been cut long ago by some men who had tried
to take cypress out of this region. They hoped to

float the logs down this corridor in freshet time. They cut the lane before they cut the trees, and the initial cost was so great that the whole project was abandoned. The swamp, therefore, remains inviolate in a peculiar sense, for it has triumphed over human attack.

We are now seven miles from the plantation house, in the very heart of a region of hushed secrecy. Here is a solitude like that of mid-ocean; a vast inland sea is here, to which the waters seem native and the trees alien. Here in this glimmering abode, apparently so remote from all exterior influences, move forces from the great Piedmont country far to the north, and from the ocean far to the south. And here Prince and I come to see the swamp in spate—I to dream and to wonder and be awed; he to be a companion, and perhaps to direct into homeward channels certain strayed swine.

# My Winter Woods

AT THE plantation gate I heard the first note of the winter's morning: a timid phoebe bird gave a plaintive call from a shadowy copse beside the road. I looked behind me across the misty cotton fields, now brown and bowed, that stretched back toward the house. In the east there was a whitening of the sky's arch, and set in it, in a space breathed clear by the wind that blows before the dawn, glittered the morning star.

The note of the phoebe, the shy woodland fragrances awaft from the great avenue before me, the mantle of mist on the cotton, the blazing star and even the bulk and blackness of the live-oak grove were elements of a type of beauty that I had loved since boyhood. But for the delicate bird note there was silence. It was the witching hour, and I was on the threshold of my winter woods.

These are the woods in which I was born and where the greater part of my life has been spent. As I go through the gate, with the glimmer of morning resting on all things, I am at home, even in the dark and solitary live-oak avenue into which I now pass.

Overhead the vast tops of these great trees shut out the sky, while far and wide their deep-foliaged limbs extend. In the cool, vaulted space under the oaks of this avenue there is ever an ancient, sequestered peace. From such old titans great limbs, larger than the bodies of ordinary trees, extend outward and upward until, passing the limbs of the neighboring oaks, they lose themselves in the shadowy merging and melting of gray moss and silvery foliage. Sometimes over their monumental frames vast networks of vines have clambered, lowering down, even in the winter, heavy tapestries of jasmine foliage starred with yellow blooms.

In the dampness and the fecund atmosphere of these woodland cathedrals, many kinds of mosses

*The Mantel and Fireplace in the Ballroom*

and lichens grow, and often the limbs of the live
oaks will be green or gray or brown—the colors of
the delicate plants which cling to and clothe the
vast dimensions of these tolerant giants. Under
such a canopy of moss and foliage both barred and
great horned owls find a congenial home. Amid
ordinary woodland surroundings owls hoot at twilight and at night only, but in a live-oak avenue
they can be heard giving their weird chorus when
the sun is still high overhead. These strange birds
interpret well one aspect of live oaks: they seem
the oracles of these dim old trees.

As I come out of the avenue the sun is rising
and the wide pinelands lie before me. All the
copses are shimmering; the dewdrops glint on the
tips of the pine needles; from the thickets of myrtle
and bay come fragrances that mingle with the spic-
eries from the pines. Everywhere, forming glimmering vistas, the pines prevail. After all, despite
the undergrowth, and despite the live oaks behind
or the watercourses grown with gum and tupelo
before, this is a pine forest. Through it one can
travel more than fifty miles in all directions, save
that which leads to the sea; and even then the pines
march down to the very beach.

I do not go far into the pineland on this winter's
morning before I come to a turpentine still, where

the work of the day is beginning. I hear the songs of the Negroes as they roll barrels or cram the little wood-burning engine with fuel. The spiciest of scents are exhaled from the shining vats.

I know the cooper at the still, so I approach his little shed which stands under a small, gnarled live oak. There is no more incorrigible optimist in the world than such a man. All day long the sturdy chopping of his broadax and the tuneful tattoo of his mallet can be heard above the shouts of the mule drivers and the creaking roll of the full barrels as they are shoved up the gangway of the still. This cooper makes all his own staves and shapes his own barrelheads. Then, with the help of a frame vise of his own design, he puts the staves together until the rondure of their arrangement makes a barrel. Forthwith, he hammers on the hoops with surprising skill and dispatch. His shop is always littered with snowy strips of pine, with slabs of dry bark, with defective staves, and the air is aromatic and resinous there. His profession must affect his character, for I never knew a cooper who was not merry. He is always singing and whistling, keeping time with his ax, his hammer or his mallet. He interprets very well the liberty, the airiness, the joyous freedom that abide in spacious forests of yellow pine.

The prevalence of these pines as a standard element of every woodland view, and as a regular background or setting for every scene, makes the winter forest here appear living and green. If there were no evergreens save the pines there might be a beautiful monotony to them; but there are many live oaks and water oaks, which are never actually bare, but which on the coming of spring reclothe themselves. The foliage of the live oak varies only in the tints of its green, but throughout the winter the water oak wears its red and gold autumn foliage.

Then there are cedars and hollies, which in this climate and soil often attain stately heights. Sometimes long, level thickets of sweet bay and myrtle will be tufted and plumed at intervals by these trees and by brilliant water oaks. Along the river, where there are sere reeds to rustle, and dry marsh and canebrakes to whisper, and immense flights of migrated wild fowl to be seen, the presence of the season is more surely felt and the minor tones of its voice are more distinctly heard. But far off in the forest, where myriads of robins are holding festivals in huge bunches of mistletoe and in tall holly trees, there seems nothing wintry save the red and white berries and the happy and excited tones of the birds.

Most of these birds are haunters of evergreen trees and bushes. Darkening the watercourse and supplying dewy retreats and fragrant sanctuaries are the myrtles, the three varieties of bay, the cabbage palmettoes, the gallberries, and the wild-tea bushes. With the pines, hollies, oaks and cedars above, and with these smaller evergreens below, the woods resemble the summer woods of the North.

And in this pine forest wild life is everywhere abundant and active; more abundant, I think, than in the summer, for in addition to the native wild things there are the migrant visitors. Birds are seen and heard everywhere—some singing and some silent, but all of them busy. Warbling sunnily, in flocks of many hundreds, there are bluebirds. There are small groups of mourning doves which feed in the pinelands on grass weeds and upon pine mast. There are meadowlarks, which find ample shelter in the yellow broom sedge. Along the edges of a bay branch I flush several woodcock that go whirling off in a glimmering flight, their wings faintly whistling. The purple finches are already eating the buds of the sweet gum and the red maple, and the ruby-crowned and golden-crowned kinglets are examining two great banners of gray moss that swing from a pond cypress.

All these birds are either watchers or watched. The watchers that I see are somewhat savage of mien: a sharp-shinned hawk darting like lightning through the forest; a Cooper's hawk perched bodefully on a low pine stump; a marsh harrier flying high over the forest, beating his way to the delta where he hunts; a red-tailed hawk circling high over the trees; a great bald eagle, somewhat out of place here, but not far from his home on the wild sea coast, pursuing a lone and splendid course above the forest.

Our familiar friend, the flicker, is everywhere to be seen in these woods; and his more handsome relative, the red-cockaded woodpecker, brightens with his presence the open stretches of pine woods. Among the other woodpeckers in the woods are the red-headed, the downy, the Southern downy, and the red-bellied. Their close cousins, the nuthatches, are here also—the white-breasted, the brown-headed, the red-breasted. Restlessness with them is a family trait shared by all the woodpecker tribe. And a cheery race they are—calling, hammering, flying hither and thither, restless, energetic, optimistic.

Turkeys and deer are the "big game" of these woods. The deer do most of their moving about at night or in those eerie half-lights which precede dawn and darkness. But sometimes the haunting charm which is conferred on woodlands by the known presence there of essentially wild life is much the same, whether the life be observed or unobserved. That deer are very plentiful in my winter woods is attested by the innumerable tracks.

I take my place beside a pine, for I have a mind to watch for fox squirrels.

I do not have to wait long, for on balmy winter days they are as restless as woodpeckers. I see a big gray one sitting on his haunches on a fallen log, thoughtfully mastering the mysterious convolutions of a pine cone; another one is coming slowly, watchfully, head-foremost, down a tall tupelo. As I can see no black squirrels from this point of vantage, I leave my log and go quietly along a dim watercourse, grown with giant short-leaf pines, maples and sweet gums. Among the clumps of gray moss on a dwarfed gum I see what I take to be a wisp of dead moss, for it is black. But then the black object takes shape. I see the rather slender tail, the delicately shaped feet a shade darker than the coat, and the telltale white ears and nose. The moment the squirrel sees me approaching he leaps to the ground. Scurrying away, he chooses the largest yellow pine in the vicinity as a place of refuge. Eighty feet it soars without a limb, and it spires forty feet above the initial branches. Up the slippery bark of this the black squirrel climbs, shrewdly keeping the immense bole of the pine between us. I time his ascent. The climb to the first limb was made in a minute and a half; and he has paused several times, not to rest, but to locate me and to set his bearings accordingly. But even the lofty refuge thus reached does not satisfy his idea of safety. I see him ascending still, past crutches of the highest desirability, until at last he has reached the very topmost frond of the pine, the slender green spire beyond which there is naught but space and blue sky. There, a hundred and twenty feet from the ground, the squirrel clings.

Continuing my walk, I come to a woodland pond. It is several acres in extent, and even to me, to whom the sight is familiar, its winter glassiness is striking. In summer black bass can be seen jumping for dragonflies, alligators swim with indolent strength on the surface or bellow grimly from its dim borders, and patriarchal frogs encircle the edges as if holding some mysterious council. But now all these are asleep, and the waters sleep with them. The wind that is swaying the pines has small effect on this pond, for the many trees densely bordering its edge and standing here and there in the water are draped in gray moss that affords a delicate but effective barrier. Of these trees the "bald" cypresses are at once striking in their appearance. Their tops are open and spread like the sequoias.

These cypresses usually have the outer layers of bark stripped off, which gives the trees a yellowish color. This is the work of raccoons and fox squirrels, that use this particular soft bark almost exclusively for bedding their holes.

A spirit broods here that is rich and sad, full of haunting pathos and romantic charm. It has a tranquility that seems entirely detached from life.

I am now within a mile of home, and the sun is not a half hour high. For my twilight watching I choose the top of a sandy ridge that falls to a deep watercourse on one side and toward level woods on the other. While I love the dawn in these woods, with the dew-hung bay bushes, the rainy fragrances and the happy activity of the birds, I love the twilight better. Some of the best hours of my life have been spent sitting on a pine log as the evening falls.

As the sun sinks behind the dark-tressed pines, there is movement everywhere in the forest about me and in the sky above me. One half of the life of the forest is looking for a place to sleep; another, the craftier and wilder, is coming forth. Every-

The Screech Owl

where birds are flying, with those subdued comrade calls that tell of the approach of darkness.
Far above the pines there is a faint, sweet whistle
of wild ducks' wings. They are hurrying, I know,
to their night haunts in the waste marshes of the
Santee Delta. The sky is suddenly darkened by a
vast flock of birds—Florida grackles, boat-tailed
grackles, red-winged blackbirds, cowbirds and
rusty blackbirds. They are going to roost in the
marshes along the river. Now, in a funereal line,
pass the black vultures in powerful flight. A covey
of quail that has been scattered by some enemy begins to call together, the sweet, querulous note of
the old female having in it a human quality. Great
flights of robins pass overhead, "changing swamps,"
or migrating from one feeding ground to another.
Befitting this hour of mystery, from the depths of
a gray swamp a great horned owl gives his far and
melancholy note.

The light in the west is fading. The voices of
the day give place to the voices of the night. In a
lone pine standing on the edge of a pond a wild
turkey has gone to roost, though I neither saw nor
heard him fly to his perch. He is restless and will
not settle on the limb, but stands there rocking
awkwardly, his long neck craned. There is a noise
in the sandy road; it is the creaking buggy of an

old rice planter driving homeward in the dusk.

Now from the shadowy watercourse below me, above whose shimmering copses a wraithlike mist is rising, two forms emerge. I thought they would come, yet I feared it might be too dark for me to see them. They are graceful beyond belief. Their movements are as fairylike as they are silent. In a little misty glade they frolic and caper like spirits of this Southern solitude. The deer are coming out of the thickets to roam the glimmering woods of night.

Their coming is the signal for my going, for now I know that there will be nothing more for me to see, save a great owl dimly brushing past on a silent wing, or a crafty fox pausing for an instant in the road to snarl at me before he vanishes into the black woods. The old planter is now out of sight and sound. The deer have vanished. The roses have faded from the great gateway of the West. The day in my winter woods is done.